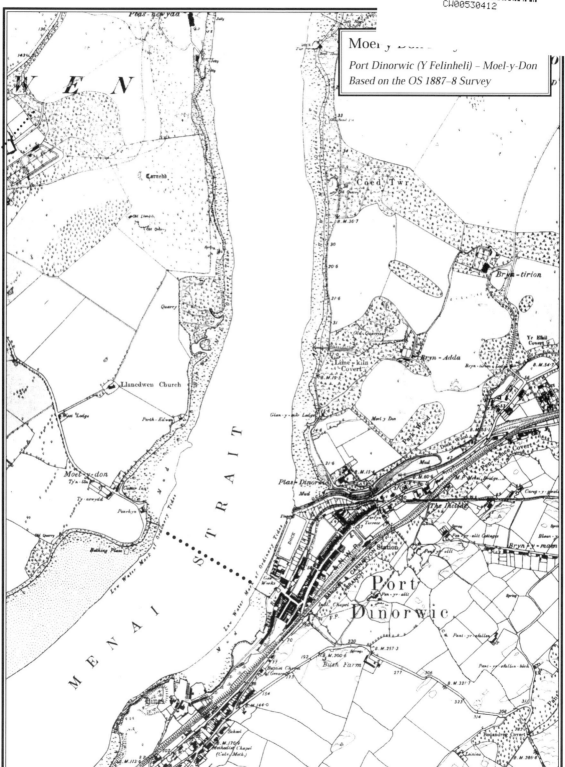

Moel-y-Don

Port Dinorwic (Y Felinheli) – Moel-y-Don
Based on the OS 1887–8 Survey

Crossing the Menai

An illustrated history of the
ferries and bridges of the Menai Strait

Reg Chambers Jones

bridge
books

Crossing the Menai – an illustrated history of the ferries and bridges of the Menai Strait
First published in Wales in 2011
By
BRIDGE BOOKS
61 Park Avenue
WREXHAM
LL12 7AW

In memory of my beloved wife
Maureen

ISBN 978-1-84494-074-5

A CIP entry for this book is available from the British Library

Printed and bound by
Gutenberg Press Ltd
MALTA

Contents

Abbreviations   4

Preface   5

Bibliography   6

Introduction   7

1: Early travel in north-west Wales   9

2: Bangor Ferries & Pier   21

3: Porthyrescob & Porthaethwy Ferries   49

4: Moel-y-Don Ferry   56

5: Caernarfon Harbour & Ferries   66

6: The Menai Bridge   90

7: The Britannia Bridge   110

8: Pleasure Steamers   132

Abbreviations

AC	Author's collection
ARO	Anglesey Record Office, Llangefni
BH	Baron Hill papers, Bangor University
BP	Bangor papers, Bangor University
BU	Bangor University
C&DH	*Carnarvon & Denbigh Herald*
CRO	Conwy Record Office
DQ	Dinorwic Quarry
FRO	Flintshire Record Office
GAS	Gwynedd Archives Service, Caernarfon
LP	Lligwy papers, UWB
NWG	*North Wales Gazette*
PNP	Plas Newydd papers, UWB
PRO	Pembrokeshire Record Office
PYA	Porth yr Aur papers, UWB
SM	Science Museum, London
VP	Vaynol Papers, Gwynedd Archives Service

Note on the spelling of place names

In various quotations the spelling of Welsh place names has been retained as in the original e.g. Carnarvon, Conway and Lleyn, but in the body of the text the same places have the modern spelling e.g. Caernarfon, Conwy and Llŷn.

Preface

ALTHOUGH THE USE OF THE FERRY SERVICES across the Menai Strait had been declining since the beginning of the twentieth century, especially as far as the commercial side was concerned, they did continue, albeit as a reduced service, until the 1950s. In its latter years, the Garth ferry, operating from Bangor pier, provided a leisurely way of crossing to Beaumaris, the Gazelle and Menai Bridge, while the Moel-y-Don ferry not only provided Anglesey quarrymen with the means of accessing the train from Port Dinorwic to Llanberis, but was also used to transport goods and animals. The Tal-y-Foel ferry enabled those living in south-east Anglesey to sell home produced goods at Caernarfon market and also replenish their weekly requirements.

Since the ferry services were once the only means of crossing the strait and were of such strategic importance, I have endeavoured to provide the reader with a little of their history.

I would like to record my appreciation of the assistance provided by the Institute of Civil Engineers; the Archivist and staff at the Library and Manuscript Department at Bangor University; the National Library of Wales, Aberystwyth; the North East Lincolnshire Museum Service; the Science Museum, London; the Archivist and staff at the Gwynedd Archives Service; the Anglesey Record Office; the Conwy Record Office; the Bangor Museum (Gwynedd Council) and the Gwynedd Archaeological Trust. Individually, I would like to thank Dr David Gwyn, Dr Katie Lench, Dr Peter Ellis Jones, David Longley, Richard Jones (Caernarfon Harbour Master) and W. Alister Williams, Sue Williams and Gwynne Belton of Bridge Books.

I would also like to thank the following for granting me access to photographs and other private material: Mary Brain, Rosemary E. A. Broadhurst, John Duggan, Colin Evans, Jonathon Evans, John Hughes, Alun Lewis Jones, Alaw Jones, E. Norman Kneale, Keith Morris, David Price, Sheila Rowland, Len Williams and Alfie Windsor.

Reg Chambers Jones
2011

Bibliography

Anthony, H, *A Brief History of the Menai Suspension Bridge*, UWB.

Baugham, Peter E, *The Chester and Holyhead Railway,* vol. 1, Newton Abbot, 1972.

Clark, Edwin, *Britannia and Conway Tubular Bridges,* vol. 1 & 2, London, 1850.

Davies, H. R., *The Conway and the Menai Ferries*, Cardiff, 1966.

Defoe, Daniel, *Tour Thro' the Whole Island of Great Britain*, London, 1724.

Demsey, G. Drysdale, *Tubular Bridges* c.*1850,* London, 1970.

Dodd, A. H., 'The Ferries', *Transactions of the Caernarvonshire Historical Society,* vol 4, pp. 98–103.

Duckworth, C. L. D., & G. E. Langmuir, *West Coast Steamers*, Prescot, 1953.

Elis-Williams, M, *Bangor – The Port of Beaumaris.*

Fairbank, William, *An Account of the Construction of the Britannia and Conway Tubular Bridges* (1849).

Harper, Charles G., *The Holyhead Road,* vols 1 & 2, London, 1902.

Hope, Bryan, *A Curious Place*, Wrexham, 1994.

Hope, Bryan, *A Commodious Yard*, Llanrwst, 2005.

Hughes, T. Meirion, *The Ferries to Anglesey.*

Husband, H. C. and R. W. Husband, 'Reconstruction of the Britannia Bridge', *Proceedings of the Institution of Civil Engineers*, part 1, vol. 58, London, 1975.

Institution of Civil Engineers, *Extract from The Britannia Bridge 1845–1850.*

Jones, Peter Ellis, *Bangor 1883–1983,* Cardiff.

Jones, Peter Ellis, 'The George Inn', *Transactions of the Caernarvonshire Historical Society,* vol. 40 p. 105.

Lloyd, Lewis, *Wherever Freights May Offer*, Caernarfon, 1993.

Lucas, John, *The Britannia Bridge 1845–1850*, The Institution of Civil Engineers.

Penfold, Alistair, *Thomas Telford 'Colossus of Roads'*, Telford, 1981.

Quartermaine. Jamie, *Thomas Telford's Holyhead Road – The A5 in North Wales,* York

Rapley. John, *The Britannia Bridge 1845–1850*, London, 2000.

Rees. James, *An Account of the Grand Flotation of one of the Monster Tubes over the Menai Straits, Britannia Bridge* (1849).

Richards. John, *Maritime Wales*, Stroud, 2007.

Rowland, K. T., *Steam at Sea*, David & Charles, 1970.

Stephenson, MP. R., *The Triumph of Science – An account of the Grand Flotation of one of the Monster Tubes – Over the Menai Straits – Britannia Bridge – June 20th, 1849.*

Thomas, David, *Old Ships and Sailors of Wales*, Cardiff, 1949 .

Thomas, David, *Hen Longau Sîr Gaernarfon*, Caernarfon, 1952.

Turner, Sir Llewelyn, *The Memories of Sir Llewelyn Turner*, London, 1903.

Wynne, John, *Hanes Sir a Thre Caernarvon*, Caernarfon, 1861.

Introduction

THE MENAI STRAIT, SEPARATING THE ISLAND OF ANGLESEY from the mainland of north-west Wales, has been both an obstacle and a means of communication from time immemorial. Tidal flow provided the means of powering mills such as Felin Heli and the many shore-line fish traps, the remains of which are still to be seen, were a major source of food supply. The extreme tidal conditions, when combined with adverse weather, presented ferry operators with very difficult working conditions. In addition, even when they were well-acquainted with the tidal problems, avoiding the many sandbanks and finding a suitable channel to cross from shore to shore made the task of carrying passengers across the Menai Strait even harder. The hundreds of sailing ships that navigated these waters also encountered many problems, particularly the underwater rocks in the vicinity of the Swellies, between the two bridges.

It is estimated that ferries have operated on the Menai Strait for over 800 years and, of the six ferries that were known to operate before 1826, the Bangor ferry became the most important as a result of the 1801 Act of Union with Ireland and the subsequent increase in traffic flowing to and from Holyhead. Although the Bangor ferry had the benefit of operating at the narrowest part of the strait, it was certainly not the most popular route with passengers due to the many operational problems. Their idiosyncratic methods of dealing with passengers ended when the Menai Bridge was opened in 1826. Although the bridge presented an easier way of crossing the strait, the remaining three ferries continued to operate until the mid-twentieth century.

A letter, dated 15 September 1978, written possibly by a local authority official, describes a ferry and the ferryman's obligations as follows:

Legal position – a 'ferry' involves rather more than merely a service provided by a boatman carrying passengers for payment – such services may exist without the rights and obligations of a 'ferry'. A ferry is in effect a special type of 'Public Highway' connecting two towns or the termini of two highways across a stretch of water. The ferry is a franchise created originally by Royal grant or by Act of Parliament. Similarly an Act of Parliament is required to extinguish or vary a ferry. The ferry ownership enjoys a monopoly – the exclusive right to carry passengers etc on the route of the ferry for which he is allowed to charge reasonable tolls. He can enforce his monopoly by injunction if necessary and the ferry owner's own neglect is no defence to this.

However in return for his monopoly he must give attendance at due times. Keep a reasonable and sufficient number of men and craft in proper order and provide such services that the public may be certain of finding the means of transport across the river. He must also provide a safe landing place. If he neglects his duty he may be indicted and fined and is open to any action by anyone as a result of his neglect.

As part of the programme of improving the roads into north Wales, Thomas Telford had the awesome task of bridging the strait. As the result of his initial design of a roadway supported by two arches being rejected by the Admiralty, the only alternative was that of a suspension bridge. Some twenty years later, Robert Stephenson, having introduced the railway system along the north Wales coast to Holyhead, was confronted with the problem of getting trains the strait. His initial design of two arches was also rejected by the Admiralty, and he decided that the railway would be carried across the strait by means of a tubular bridge.

Apart from periodic damage suffered by the Menai Bridge due to prevailing weather conditions including violent gales, it continued in operation until the early 1930s when it became apparent that the bridge, built during the pre motor car era was having to cope with an increasing number of vehicles. Even though speed and weight restrictions, as well as tolls, imposed on all vehicles crossing the bridge helped alleviate the situation to a certain extent, the number of vehicles continued to increase. As the result of an adverse engineering report on the condition of the bridge produced *c.*1935, the decision was taken to rebuild it. The work, which started in 1938, was successfully completed by the end of 1940, and brought an end to the weight restrictions, whilst the widening of the archways provided an easier passageway, especially for lorries. The tolls that had been in existence since the bridge was built were also removed.

Pleasure steamers became popular in the early part of the nineteenth century. When compared to the vessels that gave pleasure to thousands in the twentieth century, the early paddle steamers were very basic with little in the way of passenger comforts. They did, however provide an alternative means of travel between Liverpool and north Wales and enabled travellers to avoid the long tedious journey by road.

1: Early travel in north-west Wales

WALES, A LARGELY PASTORAL COUNTRY, with much of its wealth coming from the breeding of cattle and sheep, was economically backward prior to the Industrial Revolution.

The development of roads from rough tracks to those that could cope with wheeled vehicles took many years. There was little need for them in an area where the population was sparse and industry was limited to serving the local market. If merchandise needed to be transported then it would be by pack-horses that could manage to carry between one and two hundredweight. If a reasonable road had been available, that same animal would have been capable of drawing five times that figure with goods loaded onto a wheeled vehicle.

In 1555, when parishes became responsible for maintaining roads within their own boundaries, each able-bodied parishioner was obliged to devote six days a year to roadwork. Such an obligation was very unpopular as fines were imposed against the parish if a certain standard of road surface was not maintained. Even if the standard required by law was not provided, it was felt that they were adequate for local traffic needs. According to the records of the Caernarfonshire Quarter Sessions, it appeared that repairs were being carried out reasonably well even in the sixteenth century.

Such was the state of the so-called road between Chester and Holyhead in the latter part of the seventeenth century that travellers intending to cross the Irish Sea to Dublin preferred to do so by ship from Chester rather than risk the overland journey, despite the fact that navigation from Holyhead was considered much easier. Long delays could be experienced at Chester if the wind was not in a favourable direction.

In an attempt to eliminate the iniquitous costs of maintaining roads at both parish and county level, turnpike trusts were formed at the beginning of the eighteenth century. Each trust was given statutory powers (usually over a term of 21 years) to maintain certain roads to a designated standard and to cover expenditure by levying tolls on travellers who passed over each section. Although the keepers responsible for collecting the tolls had the benefit of a toll house, theirs was an onerous task since they had to be on duty day and night, each and every day of the year. Inevitably, they had to bear the resentment of travellers who were very much against the principle of tolls even though they were intended to be used to improve the condition of the roads.

The more densely populated parts of England had the benefit of roads controlled by turnpike trusts from their inception in 1709. Fifty years were to elapse before a similar trust was introduced in north Wales to cover Denbighshire and Flintshire, including the road between the Tal-y-Cafn ferry and Conwy. The road between the Bangor ferry and Holyhead (which passed through Penymynydd and Llangefni) came under the control of the Anglesey Trust which was set up in 1765. Four years later, the Caernarvonshire Trust became fully operational.

Although 452 Acts of Parliament were passed between 1760 and 1764 for the improvement of principal highways in England, the roads still continued to be narrow and intersected with ruts and miry swamps through which the progress of a wagon was difficult and dangerous. Even though road improvements usually resulted in increased trade and greater mobility, as well as easing the government's task of effective control over the region, it was strongly opposed by some to the extent of riots and bloodshed (one reason for the Rebecca Riots of 1842–3 in west Wales was the resentment felt against tollgates). Travelling on foot or horseback between towns and villages in Caernarfonshire continued to be time-consuming and involved routes that were little better than bridle paths. A Parliamentary Petition of 1769 stated that:

> … the road from Tal-y-Cafn ferry through Conway, Bangor and Carnarvon to Pwllhely [sic] is in many places incommodious and dangerous and greatly out of repair and cannot effectively be mended, widened and kept in repair … Penmaenmawr that the road is covered entirely with loose stone and broken rock which frequently falls and not only renders the road often impassable but extremely hazardous to all travellers. His Majesty's Lord Lieutenant in travelling to Holyhead to embark for Dublin have been detained at the town of Conway till the road has with infinite labour been cleared of the large quantities of broken rock and loose stones that have rendered the road for some time impassable. That the Mail and Expresses going to and from Ireland are frequently delayed by the danger and impossibility of passing this road … A new road at the foot of Penmaenmawr has been planned … with estimates to £3000. [*Journals of the House of Commons*, 28 January 1769, Vol XXXII, p.159]

As the result of a Royal Proclamation of 1635 which permitted the public to make use of Royal Posts, five main 'posts' were established within Britain with one being in Holyhead. The cost of sending a letter depended on the number of sheets of paper used and the distance to the point of delivery. The revenue realised was used to offset the cost of providing the service. Due to the state of the roads, the Royal Mail was invariably carried by post-boys on horse-back at a speed that seldom exceeded six miles per hour. This method continued until road improvements permitted mail to be carried by mail carts. Although supposedly thief-proof, robberies were such a regular occurrence in the second half of the eighteenth century that mail coaches were introduced by John Palmer of Bath in 1784. These vehicles, usually drawn by four horses, carried an impressively clad driver and guard in uniforms of scarlet coat with blue lapels and gold braid and black hat. The guard also had the benefit of an armoury which consisted of a cutlass, a pair of pistols and a blunderbuss, enough hopefully to deter any would-be thief. Only the guard was employed by the Post Office; the coach and its driver, together with the horses, were provided under contract. Although a regular non-mail coach service to Holyhead via Conwy had been introduced in 1776, it was not until 1785 that the Royal Mail began to use mail coaches along this route. The route to Holyhead via Conwy continued until 1798 when the Capel Curig route was adopted. The Royal Mail continued to be carried by road until 1846 when the service was transferred to the recently introduced railway system.

As a result of Telford's road improvements to the Irish Mail route in the early part of the nineteenth century, the time allocated for the mail coach to travel the 261 miles between London and Holyhead was 26 hours 55 minutes and this included the time allowed for the 27 changes of horses and 40 minutes for a meal stop. Meal times were taken when hostelries were reached irrespective of the time of day or night. Passengers

The Chester–Holyhead mail coach in the grip of winter. [HM Postmaster General]

who travelled inside the coach were at least protected from the worst of the weather, but those who were outside would hardly have thawed out, especially during winter months, in the time allocated for a meal. It was not unknown during the worst of the weather for a passenger sitting on one of the outside seats to be found frozen to death! The costs, including gratuities, incurred by John Bulkeley of Presaddfed, travelling by coach to Chester in 1785, were:

Bangor ferry	3s 0d
Coachman to Borth	1s 6d
Dinner	4s 0d
Fare in the Coach	15s 0d
Coachman to Bryneyed [Bryn-y-Neuadd]	1s 0d
Coachman to Conway	2s 0d
Bill at Conway	4s 9d
Maid and Waiter at Conway	1s 6d
Porter and ferry at Conway	4s 9d
Coachman to Kinmell	1s 6d
Bill at Holywell	5s 2d
Waiter and Coachman	1s 4d
Coachman at Chester	1s 0d
Porter	0s 6d

As the result of the 1769 Act of Parliament and the building of the turnpike road between Conwy and Holyhead, the first stage coach, having passed through the towns of Shrewsbury, Llangollen, Corwen, Llanrwst and Conwy, completed the journey between London and Holyhead in May 1780. This route enabled travellers bound for Ireland to avoid the notorious river crossing at Conwy ferry, and contemporary reports stated that accommodation provided at Bangor was superior even when compared with Chester. In particular, the Penrhyn Arms, a coaching inn established in 1799 at Penlon, Bangor, was a popular overnight stop. It continued as a hostelry until 1813 when it was converted by a Mr Pennant into a 'very spacious and handsome hotel with 130 beds and employing 80 servants including post-boys, waiters and maids'. It was described as '… one of the largest and best on the road with great resources in the way of reception

The Penrhyn Arms Hotel in its halcyon days, showing the gardens and path leading down to Hirael. [UB]

Above: The Penrhyn Arms, Bangor, from Telford's Holyhead Road. The entrance portico which still survives can be seen on the far right. The masts of ships in Port Penrhyn can be seen in the distance. [AC]

Left: The entrance portico, the only surviving part of the Penrhyn Arms Hotel, can be seen in the garden above the present-day A5 road. [AC]

rooms, extensive private suites for the considerable personages who travelled to and from Ireland, and stabling for over a hundred horses ...'. In 1884, the building was taken over to be used as the first home for the university college at Bangor with eleven members of staff and 58 students. It continued in use until the new purpose-built college was built in 1911. All that now remains of the old Penrhyn Arms is the original entrance arch.

The continuing government spending on road repairs, the development of toll roads and bridge-building led to improved communication between London and Dublin and the improvement of the postal service generally. According to a timetable published in 1787, road improvements enabled mail coaches leaving London at 8 p.m. to arrive in Chester at 1 a.m. on the second day, Conway at 10 a.m., Bangor at 1 p.m., and Holyhead at 7 p.m., a 47-hour journey from London to Holyhead.

Improvements were focussed on the main mail coach route and the Parliamentary Act of 1806 enabled further upgrades to be carried out to the road between the Porthaethwy ferry and Holyhead. However, the repairs carried out by the Caernarfon-shire Turnpike Trust to the roads from Caernarfon into Llŷn in the eighteenth century appeared to have been very basic and any journey, including the delivery of mail, could only be undertaken on foot or on horseback. When the semblance of a road was available, chaise-coaches were used by travellers until the 1820s when a regular service from Caernarfon to nearby towns was developed by Anthony Dillon (described in trade directories as a seedsman). The completion of the embankment across Traeth Mawr near Porthmadog (or the 'cob' as it is now generally known), in 1811 by William Maddocks of Tremadog, further improved access into the area with a turnpike road being built across the peninsular in anticipation of the development of Porthdinllaen as a port for traffic bound for Dublin.

Even though road conditions between Chester and Conwy had improved, the perilous ferry crossing over the Conwy remained. This was a most difficult ferry because of the approach to it, especially as far as animals were concerned as they literally had to be driven on board, and off again on the other side of the river. Such was the frustration of Hugh Vaughan, an innkeeper, waiting for a ferry for his customers in 1609, that he took the Conwy ferryboat without permission. The ferryman, William ap Robert, brought him to court and stated in evidence that:

> he is bound not only to transport safely all manner of the king's Majesty's liedge people, but also hath stryct chardge under extreame perill to attend & transport sodenly upon the sound of a horne or discovery of a light, at all howres of the day & night His Majesty's posts & packets passinge that way for Ireland [sic].

Things had not improved by 1813 when, according to the travel writer, Richard Fenton, 'after having our patience, tried to the utmost by waiting for about 2 hours at the ferry, [we experienced] the most unexampled and savage insolence from the ferry man'.

Having crossed the Conwy, those travelling in the direction of Bangor had the choice of negotiating Penmaenmawr, taking the Sychnant Pass or travelling along the

The alternative to the route around Penmaenmawr, the old road through the Sychnant Pass. Although taken in the late nineteenth century, this photograph of a day-trip coach making the descent, clearly shows the dangerous nature of this road.

foreshore until the road could be regained a few miles further on. The opinion of those who had travelled the Penmaenmawr route varied. Daniel Defoe, described the journey that he made in 1724 in his book *A Journey Thro' the Whole Island of Great Britain*:

> we went over the famous precipice called Penmaenmawr which indeed has made abundance more frightful than it really is; for the Rock is indeed very high and if any one should fall from it, it would dash them to pieces, yet … there is no danger of their falling; and besides there is now a wall built all the way on the edge of the precipice to secure them.

John Wesley, writing in his journal on 8 August 1756, commented about Penmaenmawr whilst travelling between Ireland and London: 'the rock runs along the side so far above the beach that one could not venture to look down'.

Prior to 1772, when a Parliamentary grant was agreed for a new road to be built, the old road, which was at a higher level, was considered to be very dangerous. Two years later, after the new road had been completed, Dr Johnson described his experience:

> we were afraid of passing Penmaenmawr over which lay our way to Bangor, but by daylight, and the delay of our coach (at Conwy ferry) made our departure necessarily late. Our coach was at last brought and we set out with some anxiety but we came to Penmaenmawr by daylight and found a way lately made, very easy and very safe. It was cut smooth and enclosed between parallel walls, the outer of which secures the passenger from the precipice, which is deep and dreadful. The inner wall preserves the road from loose stones which the shattered steep above it would pour down. The old road was higher and must have been very formidable.

The alternative to the Penmaenmawr route, namely the Sychnant pass, would have been quite formidable, especially for horse-drawn carriages dependent on an inadequate braking system. As a consolation, those who did manage it had the benefit of an inn at each end of the pass with signs that read on one side: 'Before you venture hence to pass, Take a good refreshing glass' and on the other, Now you're over take another, Your drooping spirits to recover.

Further improvements carried out by Telford were described in his report of 23 May 1829:

> a new road has been completed and opened to the public from Penmaen Bach to Penmaenmawr and the road has been widened at the summit of the rocky pass at the latter place which is also rendered secure by building a strong protecting wall along the edge of the precipice, there are still two dangerous places namely at Llanfair and Aber bridges where the approaches should be raised and a bridge is wanted where the water runs across the road.

A subsequent account written by J. Hemmingway of his journey over Penmaenmawr in 1835 stated:

> This was justly once the dread of the neighbourhood; the immense promontory affording only a narrow zig-zag path along the shelf of its side for the terrified traveller to pass ... even since the new road was cut, namely, on the 31st July 1801 during a tremendous storm of thunder, a mass of stone, supposed to weigh several thousand tons, was loosened from its bed and precipitated with a dreadful crash into the sea; ... Before this road was formed, the usual mode of going between Conway and Bangor was either in boats or waiting the departure of the tides to proceed along the sands at low water. The latter mode was frequently attended with danger ... Few carriages at that time were taken betwixt the two towns but nearly all the travellers had to go on horseback.

For travellers who had ventured over Penmaenmawr and then required to cross to Anglesey, they could do so either by continuing their journey to the Bangor ferry or take the nearer Beaumaris ferry. To reach the point where the Beaumaris ferry could be boarded, entailed walking across the Lavan Sands guided by a series of posts, when tidal conditions allowed. Needless to say, this crossing was hazardous, particularly at night. A road built in 1804 by Lord Bulkeley from Beaumaris to Porthaethwy, for the benefit of passengers and coaches crossing via the Bangor ferry, was deemed a safer route. The road from Penmaenmawr to Bangor was known as the 'Travelling Road' and that over the Lavan sands to Beaumaris as the 'Post Road'.

The road built by Telford across Anglesey to Holyhead went directly across the island, avoiding the previously established coaching inn of Gwyndy and the town of Llangefni. In place of Gwyndy, Thomas Telford built a new inn at Mona in 1822, managed by the innkeeper that had previously been responsible for Gwyndy.

The first Irish Mail coach service for Holyhead set out from London on 7 September 1808, travelling via Shrewsbury and Capel Curig. By 1810, the mail coach travelling via Chester was due at Bangor ferry at 1 p.m. where it was allowed one hour for

The Waterloo Bridge at Betws-y-Coed. [AC]

'crossing by ferry and dinner' before arriving in Holyhead at 5.30 p.m., having taken 45 hours and 30 minutes from London. The time-keeping of the coaches became so punctual that clocks and watches were adjusted in accordance with their arrival and departure

Although travelling by stage coach made the journey more comfortable, the overturning of vehicles caused by the state of the roads continued. Highwaymen and footpads were also a regular hazard. Adverse weather conditions, especially snow, caused vehicles to be engulfed in drifts for many hours or even days.

On the 20 March 1810, a committee of the House of Commons was appointed to enquire into the state of the roads between Chester and Holyhead and also Shrewsbury and Holyhead, the port considered to be the nearest to Dublin. In particular, the committee was to consider what improvements were necessary to ease travelling conditions. This long overdue enquiry revealed, not unexpectedly, that the condition of the roads was far from satisfactory. The 1815 report of the Select Committee on the Holyhead Road refers to the roads through North Wales as being in the worst possible condition:

> … exceedingly narrow (in some places but scarcely wide enough to admit two carriages to pass) and it is carried unnecessarily over many hills the ascent and descent of which are often … dangerous to travellers for where it is most narrow and most steep … it passes along the sides of precipices many hundred feet high and without any other protection to Carriages than small walls built of loose stones or very low and narrow banks of earth. An estimate to repair the road without any improvement by deviations from the present line or lowering any of the hills is £46,540-18s-7d. [UWB BP3459]

Telford's own report on the Bangor ferry (dated 8 February 1822) stated:

> Anglesey roads — Between Bangor ferry and the five mile stone from Holyhead, four out of five of the lots of the road are completed and the fifth is so nearly so that an arrangement has been made with the Trustees of the

old road to have this new road of 18 miles in length opened on the 12 May 1822 from the ferry to the five mile stone and as the new inn will be previously be habitable the travellers may be fully accommodated. The road between the five mile stone and the Stanley embankment across from that place to Holyhead has been let to Messrs Gill and Hodges.

Although Anglesey roads were not considered to be as bad as those in other parts of Wales, the comment was made that 'still the present Roads abounds with steep inclinations'. The cost of the intended work between Holyhead and Gwyndy was expected to be £3,000. From Gwyndy, the road passed over Penymynydd hills and then to the Bangor ferry. From there 'it descends … to the town of Bangor which it enters by the street between the Mitre Inn and the cathedral … From Llandegai to the next turnpike the road is very narrow [and] in many places only 16 feet … where the road is confined on one hand by Lady Penrhyn's railroad and on the other by … the Ogwen River'. The road then being described as 'continuous up the valley to Capel Curig, Corwen and beyond'.

In 1815, Sir Henry Parnell, serving on the Select Committee, recommended improvements and £20,000 was made available in the form of parliamentary grants – the sum that Thomas Telford had at his disposal when he began to reconstruct the London to Holyhead road that year. This limited the improvements to small sections but further sums that were later approved by parliament enabled him to complete most of the road from Shrewsbury to Holyhead by 1830.

The first four parts to be tackled were in the area of Snowdonia and, during the construction of the section near Betws-y-Coed, contractors paid their employees with tokens rather than cash, a method described as the 'Truck System'. These tokens could only be exchanged for goods, usually with inflated prices, at 'Truck or Tommy Shops' owned by the contractors. Wages in the form of cash rather than tokens were only made at the end of each month. A single-arch iron bridge over Afon Conwy at Betws-y-Coed bears the inscription '1815. This arch was constructed in the same year the battle of Waterloo was fought' – it was actually built in 1816.

By 1836, as the result of Telford's improvements to the Shrewsbury to Holyhead road over a period of twenty years and the building of the Menai Bridge (at a total cost of £750,000), travelling time between London and Holyhead had been reduced to twenty-seven hours. Fares for the journey between London and Chester were £3-3s-0d and from Chester and Holyhead £1-11s-6d. This reduction in the travelling time was sometimes at the expense of the comfort of the passengers and rival stage coach proprietors would enter into such enthusiastic competition to attract custom by cutting times and increasing speeds, that coaching accidents became more frequent.

Commissioners were allowed under the Turnpike Trust legislation to levy what was considered a justifiable toll on road users. The Llanfairpwll tollgate (opened in 1826) still retains the rate of charges on an external panel:

> For every Horse or Mule and Coach, Chaise, Chair or such like carriage any sum not exceeding – 4d.
> For every Horse or Mule drawing any Waggon, Cart or such like carriage with wheels of the breadth of nine inches on bottom or sole thereof any sum

The Telford tollhouse at Llanfairpwll. [AC]

not exceeding – May to September 2d, October to April – 3d.

For every Horse etc. drawing any Waggon etc. with wheels between six inches or nine inches broad any sum not exceeding May to September – 3d October to April – 4d.

For every Horse etc. drawing any waggon etc. with wheels less than six inches broad any sum not exceeding May to September – 4d; October to April – 6d.

For every Ass, Ox, or Meat Cattle drawing any carriage sum not exceeding May to September – 3d October to April – 4d.

For every Horse, Mule, Ass laden or unladen any sum not exceeding 1d, Sheep, Calf, Pig $^{1}/_{2}$d, Ox, Bull, Cow or Heifer $^{1}/_{2}$d.

Anyone refusing to pay tolls was liable to have any animal, goods or chattels seized and these would be sold within five days with the difference repaid to the owner if the toll remained unpaid. Public stage-coaches had to pay tolls on return journeys even when that happened on the same day. Various persons were allowed to travel toll free, such as clergy going to visit the sick, a funeral being held in another parish or officers and soldiers when carrying material to reopen roads or bridges.

Turnpikes were let annually either by tender or by auction and were advertised in local papers. In 1826, the following appeared in the *North Wales Gazette* showing the income generated by each tollgate for the previous year:

Gwydir gate [Llanrwst] £86	Tafarn y Grisia [Felinheli]	£113
Conway	£148	Pont Saint [Caernarfon]	£621
Penmaenmawr	£ 99	Llanaelhaearn [Llŷn]	£ 55
Bangor & Llandegai £480	Glangwna [Caeathro]	£100

By 1838, the 22,000 miles of toll roads in England and Wales controlled by 1,116 turnpike trusts, produced an annual income of £1,200,000. Denbighshire turnpike trusts ceased to function by around 1865 and the Caernarvon Turnpike Trust that had been in existence since 1769 came to an end with an announcement in the *North Wales Chronicle* on 4 November 1882 '1 November 1882 removal of the bars and turnpike gates is now being proceeded with. Travellers thereafter are able to travel along trust roads without being charged a toll'. Many of the old tollhouses then became private houses. The Anglesey Trust continued maintaining the road from Menai Bridge to Holyhead until 1895 by which time, the last of the turnpike gates had been removed on the island.

An account written by Lord William Pitt Lennox in 1863 described two brothers travelling from their school in London to Dublin to spend Christmas with their parents: They travelled by a horse-drawn coach and the journey between Dean's Yard, Westminster and Phoenix Park, Dublin took a week:

> As it was considered infradig for two such personages to travel by mail coach or stage, which we should have very much preferred, 'their Lordships' were handed over to the care of a Monsieur Victor, a French refugee who acted as a sort of private tutor. Through the kindness of the head master we were always allowed an extra week for going and one for returning…our

Carnarvonshire Old Turnpike Trust Account, 1 January to 31 December 1841. [BP UB]

conveyance was a post chaise and pair which we had to change two or three times throughout the day and the best part of an hour was usually lost in unstrapping and restrapping a portmanteau and two wooden boxes. Having got bumped over ruts or dragged through quagmires a greater peril had to be surmounted in the shape of highwaymen who infested every well-travelled road in England and levied contributions pistol in hand…Having reached Holyhead they were informed by the master of the packet '(they are) expecting you my Lords and she will get under way the moment your lordships are on board. The crossing to Ireland took from fifteen to twenty-four hours. On arrival (at Dublin) the Lord Lieutenant's carriage would be waiting for the two brothers to convey them to their parent's home.

A major source of income for the farmers of north Wales involved moving cattle to sales at autumn fairs in south-east England which could entail a trek of up to 250-miles. To cope with such an arduous journey that took up to three weeks, it was necessary for between 100 and 400 animals to be shod with suitable shoes. The route taken was usually along muddy tracks and, when toll roads were introduced, the extra costs incurred meant the old roads still tended to be used.

2: Bangor Ferries & Pier

Llanfaes ferry

DURING THE REIGN OF EDWARD I, THE THREE MENAI STRAIT FERRIES that were considered to be the most important were those of Abermenai, Porthaethwy and Llanfaes. The tenancy of the latter ferry, which is attested as being in existence in 1292, remained with the burgesses of the new borough of Beaumaris and continued as such until 1830 when it ceased to operate as the result of a declining number of passengers.

The township of Llanfaes, described as the commercial centre of Anglesey, was located in the vicinity of St Katherine's church, but the port from where ships traded during the thirteenth century was half-a-mile away at Friars' Bay on the eastern side of the island. Later, the ferry operated from the part of Beaumaris known as the 'Green', a mile or so from Fryers' Bay, but was still referred to as the Llanfaes ferry until the beginning of the fourteenth century as it was located within the parish of that name.

Travellers coming from the direction of Conwy who intended to cross the strait to Llanfaes or Beaumaris could do so by crossing the Lafan sands, a journey that could only be undertaken during the three to four hour period when the tide was favourable. The safest and recognised starting point was Aber from where it was possible to follow a series of poles in the sand to where the Beaumaris ferry could be boarded. Although this ferry was mostly for the benefit of foot passengers, there is record of a Lord Clarendon, who, having journeyed from Conwy on his way to Beaumaris, had his coach taken, presumably with wheels detached, across on the ferry.

In 1694, the annual rent paid to Beaumaris Corporation for the ferry was £8. When the Corporation provided a new boat in 1705, equipped with 'two ropes and two anchors', it was at a cost of £7-2s-9d. Within two years, a larger boat was required which cost £17-18s-3d (which was made up of £8-18s-9d for the timber, 19s-6d for its carriage and £8 for the construction of the boat). When the ferry was used for transporting soldiers across the Strait in 1699, seven shillings was charged for carrying 84 soldiers, i.e. one penny per person. The cost of transporting three horses and riders on the ferry in 1721 was one shilling, but this also covered the return journey.

The road between Beaumaris and the Porthaethwy ferry, constructed by Lord Bulkeley in 1804–5, provided an easier connection for the Irish Mail and other coaches travelling between London and Holyhead. Gradually, however, the improvements to the roads on the mainland and easier access to the Bangor ferry, resulted in Beaumaris losing its status as a post town to Bangor. Another reason for the change in Beaumaris' status was given by Browne Willis in 1721: 'The Towne of Bangor, as it lies on the Great Road from London to Holyhead, is well accommodated with inns'. The opening of the Menai Bridge in 1826 was probably the final nail in the coffin of the Llanfaes ferry and, on 7 January 1830, the *North Wales Chronicle* published a notice:

> Point ferry near Beaumaris – Notice – That the passage of the water and ferry from the point across the River Menai to the Lavan sands will be discontinued after the first day of February 1830 and the ferry cease to be

OS Map Garth Ferry. The jetty on the Bangor side can be seen just to the east of the pier on Garth Point.

worked from that day – J. Jones, Town Clerk of Beaumaris 30 December 1829. [UWB BP10082]

Garth Ferry

Garth ferry, the property of the Bishop of Bangor, was situated close to the modern-day pier, which was convenient for travellers entering the city of Bangor from the direction of Chester. It was a much safer means of crossing the strait to either the (Gallows) Point near Beaumaris or the Gazelle Inn at Llandegfan.

J. Hemmingway, writing in *Panorama of North Wales* in 1835, described an incident that occurred to a passenger in 1798:

> We crossed the Menai in order to visit Anglesey. Several ferries ply [the strait] we fortunately took that of Garth Point about half a mile from Bangor which afforded us a very curious and singular character. It is worked by an old woman by name Grace Parry more commonly called from the place of her abode, Grâs y Garth, a short, thick, squat female who, though upwards of sixty winters have passed over her head, is as strong as a horse and as

active as one of her own country goats. Her excellence in rowing and managing a 13-foot boat is unrivalled through the coast, but cannot be wondered at as she served an early apprenticeship to the business under her father and mother who lived at the same little cottage which she inhabits and worked the same passage for the best part of the last century. The prowess of her mother and skill of her father are still the favourite themes of her discourse. She remembers with particular pleasure his ability in swimming, (for he seems to have been nearly an amphibious animal) and as a proof of it, relates a circumstance that frequently occurred, even when he had passed his grand climacterick [sic]

His ferry was generally plied by the joint exertions of this couple who, upon the whole, were tolerably loving, but as storms will happen in the fairest days, so their conjugal serenity was occasionally disturbed; and sometimes an altercation would take place when they were ferrying their passengers across the Menai. In these cases, the wife, who was the better man of the two, so completely worsted her spouse in obloquy and abuse, that, unable to bear it, he would suddenly cast off his jacket leap into the Menai and swim towards his cottage, bidding his dame with a string of Welsh, execrations, take care of the passengers herself. Grace indeed seems to have imbibed much of her mother's noble spirit; and evoks [sic] down with some contempt on our set, whom she considers as inferior animals, and regards only as necessary evils. She has long been married, 'tis true, but seldom allows her husband to assist in the important avocations of rowing and fishing; because as she frankly told us, he would not do it half as well as herself.

Nothing intimidates this Cambrian heroine; she stands in fear of no human being, and is equally regardless of the rage of the elements. Last winter her boat drifted away in the night and Grace for some days thought it had been stove to pieces. However, as it was her freehold estate she made diligent inquiry after it, and at last discovered that it had been taken up and carried to Liverpool. Engaging a stout fellow in the neighbourhood to accompany her, she instantly set off for that port on foot, though nearly sixty miles distant and having recovered her property, embarked on board the skiff (although not more than twelve or thirteen feet on the keel) and with the assistance of her companion actually rowed it bask to Garth Point through heavy seas and squally weather, as perilous a voyage as ever was performed. As we found Grace's prejudices against the English rather violent and not knowing to what length they might carry her, particularly when she was under the influence of *cwrw da*, we thought it necessary for the safety of future Saxon travellers, to reward her labours with double the sum she demanded. This unexpected generosity so gratified the old woman that she swore most bitterly we were the greatest gentlemen she had ever met with, and she declared she would always like the English for our sake, and insisted on shaking hands with us individually at parting. We indulged her wish but (whether she meant it as a token of her strength, I know not) gave us each such a serious grip as almost dislocated our fingers.

The SL Mona *at the Garth Ferry jetty in Bangor. The old Penrhyn Arms Hotel can be seen in the centre distance.*
[Barbara Kelly]

Access to the ferry, which Hyde Hall had described in 1810 as 'very rough, very inconvenient and very much in need of causeways and altogether destitute of shelter', had been by footpath across fields and, despite Hall's adverse observations, it was well used. In an attempt to improve the situation, the Bishop of Bangor built a high-water stone pier in the 1830s (which was extended in timber in the 1850s) to provide access to the ferry at low water. A new road, Garth Road, was constructed in 1834 to connect the developing city centre with the section of the Penrallt estate leading to the Garth ferry jetty. This coincided with a regular sailing schedule of steam vessels being established between Liverpool and the Menai Strait.

By the mid nineteenth century, even though the old causeway which led from Garth point across the mud to deep water was described as being 'greatly dilapidated', ferry passengers wishing to board the ferry had no option but to use it. The earliest landing pier for passengers crossing on the Garth ferry was to the west of the present pier. In 1857, Thomas Morgan, who had been granted a 60-year lease by the Bishop of Bangor to operate the ferry (at a rent of £10 for the first 33 years and £15 subsequently), constructed a wooden jetty some 400-yards long from the stone pier to the low-water mark thereby giving safer access for passengers to the ferry boat.

A letter published in the *North Wales Chronicle* on 20 July 1867 from a correspondent signing himself as 'A Visitor' stated:

> I have been a visitor to this ancient city (Bangor) for the last fifty years and
> can well remember the old foot road to the Ferry and the inconvenient and

rather dangerous causeway whereby passengers had to traverse to embark by steamer to and from Liverpool. The rugged pathway amongst seaweed and shingles was so dangerous that the sturdy old sailors had often at certain periods of the tide to carry their passengers on their backs to the boats and many a mishap has taken place when the old boatmen being over burdened gave a lurch or stumbled precipitating their living freight into the mud … The old causeway it is true still remains to mark the spot of many disasters.

A further article, in the *Liverpool Mercury* on 15 August 1894, described the problems experienced by passengers requiring disembarking at Bangor:

Landing inconveniences at Bangor – The need for better facilities for reaching Bangor by sea was further exemplified yesterday afternoon. The Menai steamer leaving Beaumaris at four o'clock was unable owing to the tide, rough sea and high wind from the south-west, to get alongside the jetty at Garth Ferry and the passengers had to be transferred into an ordinary sailing boat, the process of transfer, seeing the heavy sea running, causing considerable disquietude to the lady passengers. Although the jetty was only some 30 yards from the steamer, fully that number of minutes was occupied before the passengers could get ashore. The delay might have been considerably exceeded but for the commendable conduct of the cutter belonging to the *Clio* industrial training ship which had been taking ashore some officers.

Bangor Pier

By the 1820s, a time when tourism was beginning to be established, pleasure steamers ran trips from Liverpool along the north Wales coast. By the latter part of the century the towns of Llandudno, Beaumaris and Menai Bridge had the benefit of a pier which enabled passengers to disembark and board easily and safely. Although private loading and unloading facilities were available at Port Penrhyn, not only was Bangor disadvantaged by not having a pier, it also lacked a suitable jetty for unloading freight brought by ship such as the *Prince Ja Ja*,* which ran twice weekly from Liverpool to ports along the coast. To overcome the lack of landing facilities, the corporation purchased the old slate yard at Garth in August 1891 so that the existing dilapidated jetty (which became known as the Ja Ja Jetty) could be improved to facilitate the unloading of cargo.

At a special meeting held on 22 November 1893, Bangor Town Council decided to promote a parliamentary bill authorising the purchase and running of Garth Ferry from a pier to be built into the Menai Strait. The Act was passed in August 1894 and John James Webster was appointed the engineer for the construction of the new pier. Despite an original building estimate of £13,000 for the pier and associated works, a loan of £25,000 was agreed by the Local Government Board (subject to Parliamentary approval being forthcoming), at an annual interest rate of $3^1/_2$ per cent to cover the following

* A 294-ton steel steamship (built by William Thomas & Co Amlwch) and launched 21 March 1890.

THE PROPOSED PIER AT GARTH.

TO THE OWNERS OF PROPERTY AND RATEPAYERS IN THE BOROUGH OF BANGOR.

My Lords, Ladies, and Gentlemen,

There is clearly a very great difference of opinion prevailing among all classes of the community as to the practicability of erecting a Pier at Bangor, some difference as to where a Pier should be erected, and some as to the kind of Pier suitable for the requirements of the town. About two years ago the Town Council appointed a Committee to consider this subject and to report thereon, and I understand that evidence was collected as to the cost of Piers in different watering places, and the revenue and expenditure in connection with the same. We also know that Messrs. Mayoh Bros., of Manchester, were commissioned to prepare plans of a Pier and estimates to enable the Council to obtain the consent of the Board of Trade to erect such a structure at Garth; and I now understand for the first time that they were also engaged to do other work for the Council, *for which they have never been paid*.

At the Council Meeting held on the 3rd instant, some of our Town Councillors indulged in a good deal of idle talk about misrepresentations, and Mr. Henry Lewis proposed "That the Pier Committee be requested to take steps to put the Ratepayers in possession of the facts in respect to the intention of the Council." This is what I have demanded all along, and this is what the Council ought to have done twelve months ago. On the 29th ult., I asked Mr. Henry Lewis himself, if he could give me any information on the subject, and he very candidly said that he could not do so; I have received a similar answer from other members of the Town Council. Is this right? It is a notorious fact that the question has engaged the attention of the Pier Committee for the last two years, and that they have already spent hundreds of pounds on absolutely useless proposals.

At a Meeting of Ratepayers held at the Skating Rink, on the 12th of October, the Chairman of the Pier Committee stated that the matter had been carefully considered, and that the Pier proposed by them would cost £14,000. The estimated receipts and payments were so nicely calculated as to show a clear profit of £5 a year after paying all expenses. The following are the exact figures, namely :—

ESTIMATED PAYMENTS.

	£	s.	d.
Sinking Fund to liquidate the £14,000 in 35 years at 3¼ per cent.	665	0	0
Lighting	50	0	0
Pier Master £50; Wharf Men £30	80	0	0
Establishment Charges	200	0	0
Total ...	£995	0	0

ESTIMATED RECEIPTS.

	£	s.	d.
25,000 Passengers from Liverpool Steamers at 2d. each ...	208	0	0
12,000 Passengers per other Steamers	100	0	0
18,000 Passengers per "Menai" Steamer	150	0	0
Advertising	50	0	0
42,000 Promenaders	350	0	0
Rent of Refreshment Rooms...	100	0	0
Landing of Luggage and sundries	42	0	0
Total ...	£1,000	0	0

The estimated payments are as ridiculously low as the receipts are extravagantly high. In the first place I doubt whether the Council can borrow enough money at £3¼ per cent. This I

The proposal to construct a pier at Garth, Bangor [BU]

works:

Pier and approach	£16,000
Purchase of Garth ferry and appurtenances	£ 5,500
Extending Garth wharf and jetty	£ 500
Improving of landing stage at Llandegfan	£ 300
Purchase of freehold of Gazelle Inn, improving and enlarging same; purchase of new ferry boats, steam launches etc	£ 2,700

There was vociferous opposition to the scheme as Bangor Corporation was already in debt to the sum of £100,000 and a further loan could result in an increase in the rates. Nevertheless, a public meeting voted unanimously in favour of the project:

> The Bangor Corporation (Pier, etc) Act 1894 empowered the mayor, aldermen and burgesses of the borough of Bangor to construct a pier and other works to maintain improve enlarge and extend the Garth Wharf Jetty to acquire the Garth Ferry and to improve and extend the landing place connected therewith situate in the parish of Llandegfan in the county of Anglesey and for other purposes (17 August 1894).

Included in the Act was a clause that allowed the Corporation to either discontinue the ferry service or 'from time to time suspend and again resume the working of the ferry whenever they may see fit to do so'. Furthermore, it allowed the Corporation to 'sell and dispose of the ferry boats, pontoons, landing stages and property used in connection therewith and apply the proceeds from such a sale against any borrowing related to the ferry and pier'.

The handing over of the ferry, together with freehold land, cottages and waiting room, took place at an official ceremony at Garth Point on 9 September 1894 when the Ecclesiastical Commissioners (as the owners) and William Morgan (who had inherited the ferry lease from his late father) conveyed all interest therein Bangor Corporation. At the end of the 1895 summer season, Morgan was appointed manager of the ferry at a weekly wage of two guineas. [GAS XB 2/115/35]

The corporation also purchased the freehold of the Gazelle Inn on the Anglesey side of the Strait from Mrs Salis Schwabe of Glyn Garth. [GAS XB9-15-3] and Mr & Mrs Griffith of Bootle were engaged, at a combined salary of £52 per annum (plus board and lodging and a general servant), to manage the inn and act as collectors of ferry tolls on the Anglesey side of the Garth ferry.

According to the Ferry Committee Minute Book, it was decided on 5 March 1895 that, pending the building of the pier, 'the Snowdon Steam Ship Co. be informed that the Committee are [sic] prepared for it to embark and disembark passengers, Sundays included, for 20 shillings per week'.

The pier was opened by Lord Penrhyn on 14 May 1886 and the following extract of the day's events was compiled by a local newspaper correspondent in the somewhat grandiose terms appropriate for that era:

BANGOR CORPORATION (PIER, &C.).

Parish and Borough of Bangor in the County of Carnarvon.

(Work No. 1—PIER and APPROACH.)

No. on Plan.	Description of Property.	Owners or reputed Owners.	Lessees or reputed Lessees.	Occupiers.
1	Public Roadway, Water Main, Staging and Fence.	The Mayor, Aldermen, and Burgesses of the Borough of Bangor, Richard Hughes Pritchard, Town Clerk. The Ecclesiastical Commissioners for England. William Morgan.	William Morgan.	
1a	Public Walks, Recreation Ground, Retaining Wall and Railings.	The Mayor, Aldermen, and Burgesses of the Borough of Bangor, Richard Hughes Pritchard, Town Clerk.		
2	Jetty and low water Landing Stage, Toll House, Toll Gates, Railings and Steps to Beach.	The Ecclesiastical Commissioners for England.	William Morgan.	William Morgan.
2a	Warehouse, Yard, Tramway and Fence.	The Mayor, Aldermen, and Burgesses of the Borough of Bangor, Richard Hughes Pritchard, Town Clerk.	The Liverpool, Carnarvon, and Menai Straits Steamship Company Limited.	The Liverpool, Carnarvon, and Menai Straits Steamship Company Limited.
3	Shed.	William Morgan.		The Clio Industrial Training Ship Association, Henry Thomas Brown, Honorary Secretary.
3a	Garth Wharf, Jetty, Stage and Tramway.	The Mayor, Aldermen, and Burgesses of the Borough of Bangor, Richard Hughes Pritchard, Town Clerk.	The Liverpool, Carnarvon, and Menai Straits Steamship Company Limited.	The Mayor, Aldermen, and Burgesses of the Borough of Bangor, Richard Hughes Pritchard, Town Clerk. The Liverpool, Carnarvon, and Menai Straits Steamship Company Limited.
4	Cottage, Waiting Room, Garden and Outbuildings.	William Morgan.		William Morgan. Owen Jones.
5	Urinal.	William Morgan.		The Mayor, Aldermen, and Burgesses of the Borough of Bangor, Richard Hughes Pritchard, Town Clerk.
6	Beach and Foreshore.	The Mayor, Aldermen, and Burgesses of the Borough of Bangor, Richard Hughes Pritchard, Town Clerk. The Board of Trade. The Commissioners of Her Majesty's Woods, Forests and Land Revenues. The Ecclesiastical Commissioners for England. William Morgan.		

Bangor [BU]

The weather for the Opening Day … was proclaimed 'perfect' for the thousands of people who flocked to the city in 'special cheap trains' in holiday mood appropriate to the postponed May Day. It had been deliberately delayed to include the May Day Procession in the Pier Opening Celebrations. There were men and gentlemen, women and ladies all over the place. What a capital institution womankind is especially for spectacular

The new pier under construction at Garth, Bangor, 1895 [BU]

purposes! They came out in all their bravery and it was at times difficult to say whether the women or the ladies single female in Bangor Street on Thursday who did not add her quota small or large to the general breezy sunshiny charm of the holiday … Dress colours of all shades of beautiful colour were represented in the varied phantasmagoria of the streets … Bicyclists were of course innumerable and all of sexes, ages and sizes … (the Procession included) milk-carts, American organs shown by the North Wales Music Company; elegant sewing machines exhibited by the Singer Machine Company; combined with the magnificent contingent of Messrs Thomas Lewis and Co. to produce its most salient feature … The Beaumaris Lifeboat crew … with an appeal for subscriptions to the lifeboat fund. The procession was headed by the Navy represented by about one hundred and fifty *Clio* boys with their well-known fife and drum band. The Bangor Fire Brigade with their quaint medieval flat-back caps … There was also music from Bangor Artillery Volunteers … the Menai Strait, dotted with dozens of crowded rowing boats, bird-like yachts and the gaily decked steam launch Torbay and Mona … Music accompanied the dignitaries' passage by steamer to a reception at the George Hotel while those that remained on the pier witnessed the magnificent display of fireworks on a hill near the coastguard's look-out above Siliwen road. 5,263 people used the pier on the opening day.

The 1,550 feet long pier, built by Alfred Thorne, provided pleasure steamer and ferry-boat passengers with a far easier and safer passage between the shore and vessels. Although the rowing and sailing boats that had ferried passengers across the strait continued to be used for some years, they were gradually replaced by large steam boats which were able to cope with an estimated figure of 130,000 persons intending to cross

Large crowds attend the opening of Bangor Pier [BU]

the strait each year.

The overall width of the pier was increased from 24 feet to a maximum of 52 feet and eight ornamental kiosks were spaced regularly along its length. One such kiosk, let by the corporation to a Thomas Hughes in 1897 at a rent of £20 per annum, was for the purpose of selling 'confectionary, fruit and refreshments'. [GAS XCV43]

The specially constructed bandstand and stage at the pier head enabled the Bangor Operatic Pierrot 'to provide items from the golden years of vaudeville' and for brass-band contests to be held during the summer months. The pier also provided 'an excellent platform for viewing the racing yachts on regatta day'. These and other forms of entertainment resulted in 442,000 persons patronising the pier between 1896 and 1914 as well as 296,000 purchasing contract tickets.

Following the inauguration of a summer service to Caernarfon in 1906, only an average of 4,500 ferry passengers were carried each year compared to the much higher volume travelling to Beaumaris:

Year	Adults & children
1910	42,659
1911	46,527
1912	43,167
1913	39,994
1914	41,342

The ferry service to Anglesey was popular and, until the outbreak of the First World War, carried an average of 140,000 passengers and 5,000 bicycles a year which resulted in Bangor shops benefitting from the additional patronage of the people of Anglesey as well as the passengers who came ashore from the pleasure steamers.

The pier operated without incident until 4 December 1914 when the coaster, SS *Christiana*, owned by Liverpool & Menai Straits Steamship Co, and used for transporting supplies between Liverpool and north Wales coastal towns, broke adrift and collided with it at a point between the first and second supporting towers. A temporary gangway was constructed by the Royal Engineers which enabled the pier to be used, albeit on a restricted basis.

The ferry timetable that was introduced directly after the First World War gives an indication of available routes and frequency of service:

Depart Bangor Jetty 10 a.m., arrive Menai Bridge Pier 10.20 a.m.
Depart Menai Bridge Pier 10.30 a.m., arrive Bangor Jetty 10.50 a.m.
Depart Bangor Jetty 11 a.m., arrive Beaumaris Pier 11.20 a.m.
Depart Beaumaris Pier 11.10 a.m., arrive Bangor Jetty 11.50 a.m.
Depart Bangor Jetty 12 noon, arrive Menai Bridge 12.20 p.m.

The daily service continued until 6 p.m. when the last departure was made from Menai Bridge pier. A charge of one shilling was made for each journey, except for the run from Menai Bridge pier to Beaumaris pier which cost two shillings. In July 1917, Beaumaris pier toll for all passengers arriving by ferry was raised from 1d to $1^{1}/_{2}$d but the cost for children remained at $^{1}/_{2}$d.

Until August 1917 acetylene gas lighting had been used to illuminate the Llandegfan

Excursion by horse-drawn bus ready to depart from Bangor Pier. Notices on the gable end of the house and on the side of the bus advertised the ferry service.[BU]

*Bangor Pier
entertainment. [GAS]*

or Gazelle jetty but, due to the plant that produced the gas being worn out, it was decided that oil lamps would be used until replaced eventually by electric light.

Due to the dilapidation that had occurred over the years, discussion took place in October 1920 regarding the 'reconstruction of the pier' by the firm of H. C. Pullar & Co. Ltd at a cost of £13,378-5s-0d. Whether the work was carried out is not recorded, but a note that was made two years later stated that repairs carried out in May 1922 cost the corporation £3,863. A minute recorded on 4 December 1922 stated that 'the formal opening of the reconstruction of a portion of the pier was deferred'.

An observation made just after the First World War revealed how the cost of operating the steam ferry had risen due to the price of coal. Bangor Corporation was critical of Beaumaris Council for 'exorbitant pier charges for passengers landing from ships and ferries' and 'the Militia have [sic] been disbanded which was a source of very considerable revenue to the ferry, especially as they were visited weekly by members of their families'. Passenger numbers had also been affected by the reduction in the number of mainland employees working at the Penmon Quarry in north-east Anglesey. [GAS XB2/115/331]

Although the Bangor to Beaumaris ferry made a profit of £51-6s-2d in 1925, ferry passenger numbers diminished rapidly in the 1920s due to the distance between the pier and the town centre (where a regular and convenient bus service had by then become established), as is shown in the following figures:

Year	Adults & children	Parcels	Bicycles
1921	23,563	79	89
1922	14,128	71	75

Bangor Pier entrance 1930s. [AC]

Bangor Pier in the 1950s. [Rachael Williams]

1923	6,319	276
1924	5,911	263
1925	5,242	188

Gross receipts for SS *Cynfal* for the half-year ended 30 September 1925 were:

Bangor side	£730 15s
Beaumaris side	£368 2s 3d
Llandegfan side	14s 6d
[GAS XB9-1-43]	

Returns for the month ending 16 April 1928:

	Adults & children	*Bicycles*
from Anglesey	1,537	42
from Bangor	1,425	14

Returns for the month ending 21 May 1928:

	Adults & children	*Bicycles*
from Anglesey	2,076	63
from Bangor	2,253	26

The minutes of Bangor Corporation meetings reveal that the sale or lease of the Gazelle Inn had been discussed periodically from 1920. In March 1930 a minute stated '… to allow Mr McNeil certain fixtures of furniture at the Gazelle Inn'. Since the last

The Garth ferry at the end of the Gazelle jetty. The boat appears to be the Mary Ann. *[Alaw Jones]*

The Gazelle Inn, c.1910
[Mary Brain]

The Gazelle Hotel, 1944. [Mary Brain]

Gazelle Inn - Revenue account for the half-year ended 30 September 1925
[GAS XB9-1-43]

Expenditure		
Management	£ 26 19s 4d	
Repairs and Maintenance	£ 28 15s 7d	
Trade and Working expenses	£ 7 8s 4d	
Rates, Taxes and Insurance	£ 13 10s 6d	
Stock on hand and purchases	£360 12s 11d	£437 6s 8d
Income		
Ale	£198 1s 9d	
Bottles beer & stout	£196 6s 1^1/2d	
Whiskey	£ 32 14s 11d	
Brandy	£ 9 1s 3d	
Rum	£ 9 4s 3^1/2d	
Gin	£ 3 11s 1d	
Port wine	£ 6 12s 8d	
Tobacco & cigarettes	£ 90 10s 2^1/2d	
Mineral waters	£ 16 8s 11^1/2d	
Bottles and cases	£ 5 12s 3d	£478 3s 6d
Rent for advertising	£ 5 0s 0d	
Gross Profit	£ 45 16s 10d	
To sinking fund payment and interest on loan	£219 16s 5d	
Loss to date	£173 19s 7d	

reference in the council minute book to the Gazelle Inn was in June 1930, it can be assumed that the property had been sold by then.

Due to the increasing competition from alternative forms of transport and the subsequent loss of income, partly due to the fare on the ferry having been fixed at 3d under the Bangor Corporation Act of 1894, consideration was given in 1938 to discontinue the Garth ferry. The Bangor Corporation Bill Act of 1938, if approved, would have authorised the corporation 'to suspend or modify the working of the ferry between Bangor pier and Llandegfan to sell the pier undertaking to make better provision for health government and finance of the borough and other purposes'.

Anglesey County Council was very much against the ferry service being discontinued, and asked Sir Ernest Hiley at Westminster in a letter dated 20 December 1937 to act as Parliamentary Agent for the Council in opposing Part II, sections 4 and 5 of the 1938 Act, dealing with the discontinuance of the ferry and the power to sell it. They were also against section 6 which gave Bangor Corporation the power to sell the pier. The letter pointed out that the Crown had discontinued the ferry service at Moel-y-Don but that Caernarvonshire and Anglesey County Councils had jointly purchased

Pier and Ferry employees and wages (1925) [GAS XB9-1-43]

Capt. William Owen Piermaster, £3 per week and house.

Owen Jones   Toll Collector, Llandegfan £2-3s-6d per week with
                    5s alternate Sundays and house, coal and light. Joint
                    wage for toll collector and his wife.

Mrs Jones   Manageress, Gazelle Inn, £2-3s-6d weekly with 5s
                    alternate Sundays and house, coal and light.

Gordon Jones   Toll Collector, £1-5s weekly.

Walter Owen   Toll Collector, £1-5s weekly.

John Pritchard   Ferryman, £2-9s weekly and 2s-6d alternate
                    Sundays.

Edgar Sullivan   Ferryman, £1 weekly and 2s-6d alternate Sundays.

William Pritchard   Ferryman, £2-2s-5d weekly and 2s-6d alternate
                    Sundays.

E. Roberts   Ferryman, £1 weekly and 2s-6d alternate Sundays.

A. B. Harvey   Captain, *Cynfal,* £4-2s-3d summer, £2-4s-3d
                    winter.

David Jones   Engineer, £3-8s-0d Summer, £2-11s-4d, winter.

Thomas V. Jones   Mate, £2-9s-2d Summer, £2-2s-5d winter

Thomas G. Roberts   Ferryman, £2-2s-5d.

the ferry rights with the intention of running the service. It also mentioned that the Menai Bridge was about to be reconstructed and that the work was expected to take two-and-a-half years. The letter added 'It is of the greatest importance that alternative services be maintained and possibly the Corporation would be prepared to compromise on this point, but the amenities of the Island, particularly during the holiday seasons, are being affected'.

These discussions took place at the time of the Munich crisis in 1938 and the possibility of another war. If, as the result of enemy action, the Menai Bridge were to be damaged or destroyed, a ferry service between the mainland and Anglesey would be of paramount importance. As a result of further discussion it was decided that:

> the corporation may during the months of November, December, January and February discontinue or reduce the ferry service having given the public seven days notice. A full service is to be resumed if asked by the Caernarvonshire County Council or Anglesey County Council or in any emergency that required the service of the ferry.

During the war, the pier decking was removed in accordance with a War Office directive as a precaution 'against the enemy making use of the pier to invade Bangor'. In 1945, Iorys Hughes, a consulting engineer (a native of Bangor who had been involved with the design of the wartime Mulberry Harbour), was asked to inspect the pier and estimate the cost of reconstruction. Possibly due to its state and as a matter of expediency, the sum of £6,350 was provided to carry out the repairs recommended by him.

The Garth ferry boat Mary Ann, arriving at the Gazelle jetty. *[AC]*

Due to the pier's deterioration over subsequent years, a report was produced in July 1971 by a firm of Liverpool consulting engineers, which concluded that 'the pier at that time was dangerous in several respects and public assembly thereon should not be permitted'. The cost of reconstruction would be £260,000.

As a result of the continuing operating losses of the Garth ferry a meeting, chaired by Councillor C. G. Gibbs, Chairman of the Bangor Pier Development Committee, was arranged with representatives of Beaumaris Borough Council, Menai Bridge Urban District Council and Bangor Borough Council at the Town Hall, Bangor on 16 January 1973 to consider a joint scheme with Beaumaris for the running of the ferry boat and to share costs. However, as the result of Bangor Council purchasing the ancient Glyn Garth ferry in 1894 under the provision of the Bangor Corporation (Pier etc) Act of 1894, it was necessary for it to consider its statutory obligations with regard to providing the ferry service. These included maintaining the ferry service during eight months in any one year and under section 4 of the Act, the Council was required to keep the ferry in readiness at all times and in good repair and have available the necessary staff to work the ferry (due to loss of traffic, the Bangor Corporation Act 1988 allowed them

Expenditure relating to the ferry 1972/73 (prices quoted are post decimalisation)	
Boatmen – Wages etc	£575.45
Insurance & Licences etc.	£ 80.02
Oil	£ 49.06
Repairs and Maintenance	£819.99
Tools and Equipment	£ 31.69
Printing and Stationery	£ 2.53
Miscellaneous – Boatmen's Licences	£ 6.00
Income from sale of ferry tickets	£601.61
Net Deficit 31.12.72	£963.13

to either discontinue or reduce services during the months of November, December, January and February).

Although consideration had been given by the Council to promoting a private bill to discontinue the ferry service, it was emphasised that the purpose of the meeting was to consider the possibility of a joint scheme between the three councils to run the ferry boat between Bangor, Beaumaris and Menai Bridge. Bangor would continue to be responsible for the statutory ferry service between Bangor and Glyn Garth. Since the pier had been closed and the ferry could only operate from the jetty for a period of six hours, i.e. three hours before and after high tide, this presented problems for passengers arriving and departing from Bangor. During the discussion which ensued, the following points were raised:

1. It was indicated that Bangor would be the key factor if a joint scheme was agreed upon. However, due to the lack of facilities at Bangor and the closure of the pier, the ferry service could only be operated from the Bangor jetty when the tides were favourable (i.e. 3 hours before and 3 hours after high tide). This would cause difficulties for passengers wishing to land at Bangor. The members agreed that this was a valid point. The Chairman stated that the Bangor Council were in fact considering the future of the Pier and there was a possibility that the Pier would be opened again in the future.

2. Arising from the above the question of the feasibility of providing an extension to the present Jetty was considered. However, due to the high cost involved and the danger of a hazard to shipping it was considered that it would not be possible to extend the Bangor Jetty.

3. It was felt that in the past sufficient publicity had not been given to the ferry service and should an agreement be reached by the three Authorities concerned serious consideration should be given to adequate publicity for the ferry service.

4. Reference was then made to the Officers' Meeting when it was suggested that a private company be approached to operate the ferry service. After a lengthy discussion it was felt that the suggestion could not be implemented for the forthcoming season because of the time factor. However, in the meantime enquiries should be made on these lines.

5. The Deputy City Treasurer submitted a financial statement showing the income and expenditure incurred in running the ferry service during the financial service during the financial year. As the statement showed the expenditure appertaining to the use and maintenance of two ferry boats the Deputy City Treasurer was requested to submit an amended statement showing as accurately as possible the expenditure involved in the running and maintenance of one ferry boat and that this statement be circulated to both Anglesey Authorities.

6. It was agreed that as the members did not have delegated authority to

determine this matter the points discussed should be reported to the appropriate Councils with a view to a joint scheme being introduced for the forthcoming season as an experimental period and that a further Meeting be arranged of this Joint Committee as wish to participate in the scheme.

At a meeting held on 8 March 1973, the decision was taken to participate in the scheme for a trial period of twelve months. It was also necessary to take into consideration Value Added Tax that was being introduced on 1 April 1973 as far as ferry fares were concerned. [GAS XB9-16-17]

The City Treasurer's report, dated 11 February 1974, showed that during the period when the ferryboat *Nantlys* operated between Bangor, Beaumaris and Menai Bridge, from 27 May to 14 September 1973, the income and expenditure account showed a deficit of £826.59. In accordance with the agreement made on 8 March 1973 that such a deficit would be apportioned pro rata to the town's population, the allocation was made as follows: Bangor BC £606.54, Beaumaris BC £97.30 and Menai Bridge UDC £122.75. The Garth ferry service ended with the sale of the *Nantlys* in 1976.

Subsequent years saw a steady decline in the state of the pier until 1982 when enquiries regarding its restoration revealed that it would cost £750,000. Undaunted, an ad hoc committee of the council launched an appeal and sufficient monies were raised to enable the pier to be restored. Sadly, neither the Garth ferry nor the pleasure steamers that had been regular callers in the past were to share in this investment. The pier was reopened on 7 May 1988.

Garth ferry boats

The surviving records relating to ferry boats that operated between Garth, Llandegfan, Beaumaris and Menai Bridge indicate that, prior to 1896, passengers relied on rowing or sailing boats with no protection being provided from adverse weather. Even after purchasing steam-powered vessels to cope with increasing number of ferry passengers, rowing and sailing boats continued in use whenever possible because of their lower running costs.

SS *Torbay*

The Bangor Council Pier and Ferry Committee recommended on 14 December 1894 that

> the Council purchase a steamer or steamers suitable for working the ferry and other purposes … 19 February 1895 SS *Torbay*, a 19-ton wooden ketch-rigged steamer to be inspected in Manchester by Mr John Jones (of the Antelope) and if in order offer £700'. Built in Paignton in 1892 and fitted with a 20hp single compound engine, her measurements were: length 64ft breadth 13ft and deck to keel 12ft. With a crew of four, she was authorised to carry 150 passengers. The *Torbay* was purchased for £725 from H. E. Moss & Co. Ltd, ship brokers, and insured for £800 for the journey from Liverpool to Bangor. Mr J. Gill, Bangor Borough Surveyor advised the Council that the vessel 'had been used for traffic in the English Channel at Torquay.'

The Garth ferry boat Torbay *approaching the* Clio *training ship. [Llew Williams]*

It was decided at a meeting of the Pier and Ferry Committee on 26 March 1895 that 'the Town Clerk be appointed managing owner of the *Torbay* for the purpose of registration at the Port of Beaumaris'. [GAS XB2/115/35]

The *Torbay* inaugurated a ferry service to Beaumaris, initially during the summer months and later a skeleton service during the winter. The intention was to run the ferry to Beaumaris each day of the week, but the Beaumaris pier authority refused to allow the vessel to disembark passengers on Sundays. It was decided in December 1907 that the *Torbay* would continue to provide a winter service on Fridays and Saturdays until the end of December when the service would be reviewed.

The decision was made to sell the vessel in October 1915 but this was postponed because of problems with the delivery of the new ship *Cynfal*. *Torbay* was eventually sold to Ivor Taylor of the Isle of Man for £80 on 16 March 1918. [GAS XB2/115/38]

SS *Menai*

There is no record of Bangor Corporation owning a steam vessel called *Menai* but a vessel of that name is mentioned several times in the Bangor City Council minutes. In February 1895, in answer to a question posed by Councillor P. S. Gregory, 'what offer had been made to the Council with regard to the *Menai* steamer', he was advised that no communication had been received with regard to the vessel … and that the Pier Committee was quite clear that they did not want to purchase the *Menai* and *Pioneer* steamers'. A letter dated 26 March 1895 from Mr T. Hughes of Beaumaris asked what the terms would be if 'the SS *Menai* made use of the present or new pier'. The vessel is again mentioned on 20 May 1895 when the ferry committee decided that 'the pier toll for SS *Menai* passengers using the jetty place at Bangor be charged 3d each way, this to include landing or embarking in boats'. [GAS XB9/4/1 and *North Wales Chronicle* 2 March 1895]

The bill of sale for the Garth ferry boat Torbay. *[GAS]*

SL *Mona*

A reference, dated 22 January 1896, in the Pier and Ferry Committee Minute Book stated that a vessel named SL *Jubilee* was to be given a week's trial and, if a favourable report was received both as to its performance and its condition, then it would be bought for £150. Authorised to carry 38 passengers, the steam launch was eventually purchased in June 1896 and renamed SL *Mona*. The ferry sank at her moorings in a gale on 20 February 1916 but was successfully raised to continue in service until 1920 when she was put on sale at W. H. Rowland's wharf in Bangor

SS *Lady Magdalen*

Originally named *Clutha No. 11* (official number 106013), she was built by Russell & Co. of Port Glasgow, at yard Nᵒ 398, for the Trustees of the Clyde Navigation, Glasgow in 1896. The steel 44-ton twin-screw steamer had the benefit of two sets of compound engines manufactured by Muir & Houston, Glasgow which produced a speed of 10 knots. She was sold to Bangor Corporation in July 1904 for £1,400 and insured for the same amount for her journey from Glasgow to Bangor. A letter dated 26 January 1904, from Hugh Pritchard, Mechanical Consulting Engineer at Port Dinorwic drydock, stated '*Clutha No. 11* … arrived in Bangor on Sunday morning last having made the run from Greenock, in 26 hours without a hitch'.

The former Garth ferry boat Lady Magdalen *operating at Neyland, Pembrokeshire in the 1930s. [Pembrokeshire Record Office]*

Registered in Beaumaris, she was renamed *Lady Magdalen* a month after her arrival in Bangor. In addition to her normal ferry duties, she carried passengers twice a day, Mondays, Wednesdays and Saturdays, on trips along the strait during August. On some of the summertime trips, the passengers were entertained by a 'band of three instrumentalists' performing on board. In addition, the vessel, under the charge of Robert Hughes (who was also a Menai Strait pilot), took passengers on occasional evening excursions from Bangor to Caernarfon and back at a cost of five shillings per person. For the privilege of landing or embarking passengers, Hughes had to pay Caernarfon Harbour Trust dues amounting to £20 for a season. [GAS HD15/2/2]

In October 1917, it was necessary for *Lady Magdalen* 'to be put in order to meet the requirements of the Fishery Board' and the work was carried out at the Port Dinorwic dry dock. [GAS XS1243] Although placed in the hands of four brokers with the intention of selling her, she was requisitioned in February 1918 by the Admiralty at a 'rental' of £80 per month and an armed tug arrived to convey her to Liverpool. Subsequent to her release in May 1919, and due to the 'dilapidations' that she suffered, the Admiralty paid the corporation the sum of £300 as compensation. She was sold the following month for £3,100 to Middlesborough Corporation and re-registered in the town. By 1934, although still registered in Middlesborough, she was purchased by Frederick R. Lee, ferry proprietor of Pembroke Dock. In 1947 she was sold to British Conveyances Ltd, of Newport, Monmouthshire and registered at Newport. Pembrokeshire County Council purchased the vessel 12 January 1949 and retained ownership until 1959 when she was sold to Hancocks a local ship building firm. [GAS XB2/115/38]

SS *Cynfal*

An order was placed with Yarwoods of Northwich for a new steamer to be built for £3,500 with the capability of carrying 240 passengers. Payments were made by instalments depending on the progress of the vessel. Although the decision was made by the council to purchase the new ferry in March 1915, she was not delivered until June 1917 when the final instalment of £989-19s-2d was paid. Since the delivery was taking place during wartime, she was insured at a cost of £5-12s-7d against 'attack by aircraft and bombardment' during her voyage to Bangor. She was requisitioned for war service by the Ministry of Shipping in February 1918 for which the corporation was paid

£2-2s-0d per day. Her role consisted of ferrying sailors from shore to vessels in the Firth of Forth. Captain Harvey, who continued to be in charge of her, was provided with a uniform and paid £5 per week for about 'five hours of work per week'. However, for some unexplained reason the *Cynfal's* crew had gone on strike and left the ship unattended but, on returning to Bangor, they were told that there was no work for them. The ship was released by the Admiralty in March 1919.

Whenever straightforward maintenance work had to be undertaken to the ship's hull, a cradle was put at her disposal at Hirael, Bangor, 'under the Old University' [Penrhyn Arms]. When the decision was made for the now defunct industrial training ship *Clio* to be broken up, the corporation approved an application for the *Cynfal* to tow the vessel on 16 March 1920 up to the Ja Ja jetty. *Clio's* anchor was not removed from the jetty until six years later. Due to the decline in the number of passengers, a decision was taken in May 1920 that *Cynfal* cease operating as a passenger ferry. Nevertheless, twelve months later, consideration was given to converting the vessel 'into an oil-driven boat'. There is no record as to whether the actual conversion took place, but she continued carrying passengers until 18 June 1929 when she was sold for £600 to the James Dredging, Towing and Transport Co. of Westminster and re-registered at the Port of London.

ML *Menai*

The *Silver Queen*, described as an 'army boat', was purchased from Lewis O. Evans in July 1921. Although initially renamed *Mona,* followed by *Menai*, she continued to be referred to as *Silver Queen* in the council minutes. She was used both as a ferry and for pleasure trips until April 1930 when she was sold for £133.

ML *Nantlys*

W. H. Rowland of Garth boatyard, Bangor, who had declined the post of consulting engineer offered to him by Bangor Corporation, accepted their request to design a motor vessel suitable for use as a ferry and capable of carrying fifty-five passengers and a crew of two for a fee of £10-10s. He submitted the design and specifications to three boat builders and subsequently presented the council with three tenders from Crosfields of Conwy, £797 (delivery end of September); Rowland Dockyard Co. of Bangor,

(delivery in ten weeks) £1,050; and Matthew Owen & Son of Menai Bridge (delivery in three months), £725. The latter tender was accepted and the *Nantlys*, as she was named, was used as a ferry until 1976 when she was withdrawn from service.

Other boats involved with the ferry service from Garth, Bangor were:

The Nantlys *with Norman Williams aboard.*
[John Duggan]

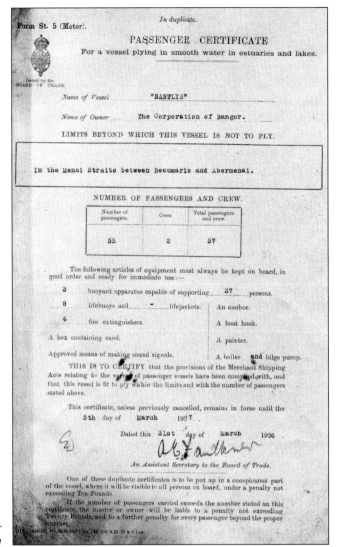

The Nantlys *passenger certificate. [GAS]*

Miss Evelyn (1902–09)
Sarah (1902–09)
Mary Ann (1908–24 authorised to carry 30 passengers)
Clumsy (1917–23 authorised to carry 45 passengers)
Birmingham City (twin Atlantic diesel engine – 1935, £377)
Dumpy
Pirate
White Thistle (1918–19)

Lewis O. Evans

Soon after Lewis Evans purchased the Old Baths cottages at Garth in 1928 he sought permission from Bangor Council to 'reconstruct a jetty and lay stepping stones upon the

Boat repairs near the Old Baths cottages, Garth. Bangor pier is under construction in the background. [Colin Evans]

foreshore below high water mark' at Siliwen, in order that he could operate a private ferry service from the Old Baths to Anglesey and run pleasure trips along the strait. After an inspection of the area by the Pier and Ferry Committee, it was recorded that 'there is no vestige of the old pier removed about 35 years ago…the proposed jetty will be an obstruction to boating on the straits …' However, a letter dated 20 January 1925 from the Board of Trade stated that the council's objection to the building of a jetty was invalid. As a result, Lewis Evans built his jetty conveniently close to his home and by the following year had purchased a boat suitable for the intended ferry service.

A Bangor Corporation minute of 21 May 1929 refers to Lewis Evans seeking permission to convey parties from Glyn Garth (where the Fellowship Holiday Association had been established) to Siliwen Baths in his boat, the *Mary Pickford*. Although this was declined, Lewis Evans continued operating his unauthorised ferry. Realising that Evans was determined to continue carrying passengers, a council minute noted that 'the committee are [sic] prepared to arrange facilities for this if he [Lewis Evans] will consult with the treasurer and Piermaster who have been empowered to act'. It was recorded in March 1930 that, due to Evans continuing with his 'ferry', the Town Clerk was asked to advise the committee on the purported 'infringement of the [Bangor] ferry rights'. Again officialdom tried to obstruct Evans's endeavours by preventing him landing

The amended OS map, sent by Lewis Evans to the Mercantile Marine Department in support of his 1924 application for a ferry licence . [GAS]

The application for a ferry licence sent by Lewis Evans to the Mercantile Marine Department in 1924 . [Colin Evans]

passengers from his boat at the pier until advised by the Town Clerk that he could not be refused such landing facilities provided he made the requisite payment. Six years later, infringing or not, Evans was still ferrying people, not only to Glyn Garth, but also to Beaumaris and Caernarfon.

During his lifetime, Lewis Evans (who died in 1956), had carried on business as L. O. Evans & Sons which covered a number of activities including operating pleasure trips on the Menai Strait during the summer months in one of three motor launches that he owned. The trips, which were stated to be 'extensively supported by the public', were based on the then three jetties built at the Old Baths under the Board of Trade licence. In addition, moorings, which came under Evans's jurisdiction, were provided for sailing and fishing boats at the Old Baths. Facilities were also available for storing such vessels during the winter months, including those of the university sailing and rowing clubs. The cost of mooring and storage ranged from £5 per annum for the smallest boats to £20 for the largest. Income was also derived from the gathering and selling of shell fish from the Menai Strait under licence of the Lancashire and Western Sea Fisheries Board.

On 16 November 1959, Bangor Council served a notice in respect of the cottages at the Old Baths under the Housing Act 1957 which stated that the four cottages were unfit for human habitation. Fortunately for the Evans family, the Council failed to take steps to implement the order for compulsory purchase of the Old Baths. On further enquiries being made by the Evans family in 1964, it was established that since a period of three years had elapsed since the compulsory order was originally made, it could not be implemented.

The Mary Pickford *ferry boat outside the Old Baths, Garth. [Jonathon Evans]*

One of Lewis Evans'
ferry boats at the Old
Baths, Garth. [Colin
Evans]

During the period of uncertainty that the Evans family had to endure with regard to the compulsory purchase, the decision was taken to discontinue their maritime activities and concentrate on haulage contracting and the refurbishing of the Old Baths property.

Passengers and
helmsman aboard one
of Lewis Evans' ferry
boats at the Old Baths,
Garth. [Colin Evans]

3: Porthesgob & Porthaethwy Ferries

Porthesgob Ferry

FIVE OF THE SIX MENAI STRAIT FERRIES, DESCRIBED AS CROWN FERRIES, were controlled by royalty. The sixth, the Porthesgob ferry, was the prerogative of the Bishop of Bangor and his successors. When questioned as to the validity of such a claim, Bishop Matthew Englefield (1328-1357)* referred to the Black Prince's charter of October 1351 which gave him and his successors 'a certain passage of theirs across the water of the Meney [sic] near the town of Bangor called Porthesgob and all the commodities of whatsoever kind to their said passage'. Included amongst the various properties held by the Bishop of Bangor were three small units known as Cae Coch Gorad y Git and Cae Glowr where a ferry pier and inn were later constructed.

The area of operation of Porthesgob ferry had been a contentious issue for many years until it eventually led to litigation in the sixteenth century which resulted in the Bishop of Bangor re-establishing possession. Compared to the Bangor (Porthaethwy) ferry, with its well-defined line of operation and terminus at Borth (below the present Bodlondeb property on the mainland), the Porthesgob ferry had no clear territorial limits. In accordance with the liberties granted in the charters of the thirteenth and fourteenth centuries, the Bishop of Bangor claimed all landing places on Anglesey between Cadnant and Gallows Point in Beaumaris as well as between the Porthesgob jetty and Garth, near the present-day Bangor pier. In reality, one ferry plied between

Cadnant, Menai Bridge where Porthesgob ferry passengers embarked. [John Hughes]

*There were two Matthews in office: It appears that the dates relate to Matthew Englefield (1328–57) rather than Matthew Hutton (1743–47).

Comparative figures of fares collected by the two ferries on fair-days:

	Porthaethwy	Porthesgob
1303	10s-0d	4s-2$\frac{1}{2}$d
1304	14s-11$\frac{1}{2}$d	6s-7$\frac{1}{2}$d
1307	18s-11$\frac{1}{2}$d	7s-10d
1308	18s-11$\frac{1}{2}$d	7s-10d
1309	18s-10d	8s-9d
1312	20s-0d	10s-0d
1313	15s-10$\frac{1}{2}$d	5s-6$\frac{1}{2}$d

The total annual receipts for the two ferries on fair-days gradually decreased from 24s in 1314 to 8s-4d in 1352. [Ministers' Accounts – General Series 1227/3 PRO]

Gorad y Git (below Upper Bangor) to Cadnant creek on Anglesey and the other for foot passengers from Garth point to the Gazelle Inn at Llandegfan on the opposite shore.

In the early eighteenth century, at the time when both Porthaethwy and Porthesgob were controlled by a joint tenancy, a new ferry pier was constructed on the mainland below Cae Glowr on the mainland for the joint benefit of the two ferries. This new terminus enabled larger ferry boats to be brought into service with the capability of transporting an increasing number of carriages and wagons across the strait especially from 1740, by which time there was a regular wagon service between Chester and Holyhead. As a result of Beaumaris having lost its status as the post town to Bangor in 1718, mail for Ireland came via the city as did the first Irish mail coach to leave London for Holyhead in October 1785. William Turner referred to a journey that he made c.1790 from Ireland to his home at Parkia in Caernarfon: '[I] rode across Anglesey, crossed of course in the flat boats at Bangor Ferry, where the George Hotel is, and rode on'.

During fair-days in May and October, the income realised by the Porthesgob ferry was approximately half that of the Porthaethwy ferry. This may be due to the fact that the crossing between the mainland and Cadnant on Anglesey was twice as far as that of the Porthaethwy crossing. Porthesgob also had the disadvantage of being exposed to the prevailing south-westerly winds making it difficult to row across the Menai.

No doubt aware of the growing number of customers requiring crossing to Anglesey, John Ewar, Bishop of Bangor commissioned the building of an inn above the new ferry pier on the fifteen acre site at Cae Glowr in 1771 during the reign of George III at a cost of £300. Named the George Inn, the tenancy was let to William Jackson who held it for 45 years until his death in 1827. During this period, there was considerable growth in the number of travellers who stayed there and appreciated the standard of service provided and it would appear that the George specialised in 'catering for the wants of the upper echelons among the travelling public at that time'. Jackson took every opportunity of improving both the building and the surrounding grounds. It was described in 1791 as 'an elegant inn amongst trees and green fields with a neat garden

George Hotel, July 1844. This building appears to be smaller than the one portrayed in the photograph below. The path leading down to the ferry jetty can be clearly seen.

in front which invites you to experience the cleanliness and comfort of its accommodations'. Although the hotel's prices were thought to be very high bearing in mind its location, the accommodation was described as being extremely good and on a par with 'most of the inns upon the great roads near London' and was well patronised (it eventually became the George Hostel, part of the Bangor Normal College, in 1919).

As a result of the joint tenancy of the Porthesgob and Porthaethwy ferries not having been renewed, disputes regarding their operating territory recommenced. The fact that both parties used the same pier did nothing to ease the situation. William Davies, tenant of the Porthaethwy ferry in 1772, challenged in the courts the right of the Bishop to operate so close to his ferry. When the judgment was given in his favour, Bishop Ewar had no option but to cease operating the ferry between Cadnant and Cae Glowr on the 18 August 1772.

George Hotel, a mid-nineteenth century engraving. The people on the shore are standing close by where the ferry jetty would have stood.

GEORGE HOTEL, BANGOR FERRY, NORTH WALES.

IMPORTANT TO CAPITALISTS, HOTEL KEEPERS, AND OTHERS.

PARTICULARS AND PLAN
OF THE WORLD-RENOWNED

GEORGE HOTEL, BANGOR FERRY,
ON THE BANKS OF THE MENAI STRAITS.

TO BE SOLD BY AUCTION,

BY

MESSRS. WILLIAM DEW & SON,

ON THE PREMISES,

On SATURDAY, the 7th day of APRIL, 1877,

At **TWO O'CLOCK** p.m. most punctually,

Subject to Conditions then and there to be produced,

THE ABOVE DELIGHTFULLY SITUATED AND FASHIONABLE

FREEHOLD HOTEL,

With extensive and charming Grounds, most tastefully laid out, covering an area of upwards of 13 Acres, with Kitchen and Flower Gardens, Conservatories and Vineries, approached by a Private Drive with a Lodge at the entrance. This far-famed resort is close to the Suspension Bridge, and within easy distance of the Britannia Tubular Bridge.

The Hotel contains a Public Drawing Room, 31ft. 8in. by 30ft. 7in.; Coffee Room, 58ft by 34ft.; Nine Private Sitting Rooms, and makes up 76 beds. It has also a large Kitchen recently erected, with all domestic offices necessary to so large an Establishment, and good Cellars. There is a handsome detached Billiard Room and Smoke Room.

The Outbuildings comprise Eight Cottages for out-door Servants, Stabling for Twenty-one Horses, Harness Rooms, Coach-houses, Cow-houses, Barn, Granary, and a well-placed Tap-room.

The whole of the premises are lighted with Gas made on the premises.

There is good Spring Water on the premises, and there is also a constant supply of good Water from the Bangor Waterworks.

The sheltered situation, and the mildness of the climate, is such that the Hotel is admirably adapted as a Winter Residence for visitors.

The sale will include all the Furniture, Trade Fixtures, Wines, Stock-in-Trade, and Out-door Effects, at a valuation to be made by the Auctioneers, the amount of which (exclusive of consumable articles) will be declared at the time of sale, and an inventory will be produced.

An admirable opportunity is now presented to Hotel Keepers and others, as the George is one of the oldest-established and most frequented Hotels in the Principality.

It is accessible from Liverpool by steamer, and by rail from all parts.

The Hotel is now in thorough working order, and may be viewed at any time.

Possession can be had on the 9th of June next, which will give the Purchaser the benefit of the ensuing season.

These Particulars and Plans, and any further information may be had from Messrs. W. & H. T. BROWN & ROGERS, Solicitors, Chester; the AUCTIONEERS, Wellfield House, Bangor, and Town Hall, Rhyl; and from

Messrs. **HELPS, BIRCH, CULLIMORE, & DOUGLAS,**

Solicitors, Chester.

Sale particulars of the George Hotel, April 1877. [UB]

George Hotel and the jetty on the Caernarfonshire side viewed from Menai Bridge. [John Hughes]

Porthaethwy Ferry

Land associated with the Porthaethwy ferry extended from Carreg-yr-Halen to Porth Daniel and those who needed to cross the strait had the choice between the former, which is to the west of the present suspension bridge, to Treborth Mill on the mainland or by taking the main ferry from below the Cambria Inn (once known as the 'Three Tunns') at Porthaethwy to the terminus at Borth which lies below the present Bodlondeb property. Although the distance at high tide of 330 feet between Carreg-yr-Halen and Treborth Mill was similar to the main crossing, the former was particularly dangerous since the question of timing was important due to the strong currents and dangerous tides. Until the Menai Bridge was built, it was the custom for cattle to be made to swim across the strait at the location of the Porthaethwy ferry (or Bangor ferry as it was also known as) when being moved to or from Anglesey. Timing would be particularly important to ensure that cattle were driven into the strait by their accompanying drovers in order to take advantage of slack water. If any appeared to be being carried along by the tide, herdsmen in small boats would throw a rope over their horns and drag them ashore.

During the reign of Edward I, the annual income from the Porthaethwy ferry was 86 shillings, but by 1352, it had risen to 90 shillings. The Crown's share amounted to £2 3s 0d out of which the King was responsible for half of the cost of the ferryboat and other expenses pertaining to its upkeep. The remainder of the income was retained by the ferry tenant.

In 1629, considering Porthaethwy to be an easily realisable asset, King Charles I decided to sell the leases to private speculators and thereby established the method of operation which was to last for over 300 years.

With increasing use being made of the Conwy to Holyhead road as the result of the gradual improvements, a 1777 publication for the benefit of those travelling between Conwy and Holyhead, stated:

To Bangor 16 miles. At the Eagles you will be tolerably accommodated.

To Bangor Ferry 1 mile. There is an inn each side of the ferry. The house on the Anglesey side has been much neglected. That on the Carnarvonshire side will, when finished, be fit for the occupation of travellers.

To Gwyndy, the Halfway-House 12 miles and a half. This is in every respect the best and cheapest house on the road.

To Holy-Head 12 miles and a half. At Holy-Head, the Eagle and Child, the principal inn built by Sir J Stanley, contains elegant accommodation for travellers and good entertainment. There are two other good inns in the town.

NB The road from Chester to Holy-Head is in general a fine turnpike road, but at the ferries and on the road you meet with great imposition. They charge the travellers in carriage 1s a piece at each ferry, whereas they ought to demand no more that 1d and 2d for a horse.

Periodic complaints against the Porthaethwy ferry operators were usually dealt with by a committee of local landowners. A meeting of the 'Gentlemen of the county of Anglesey' with Owen P. Meyrick, Esq., in the chair was held at Gwyndy on the 14 October 1782, to consider:

> the several complaints of imposition, delay and ill treatment experienced by the public at Porthaethwy Ferry … the said ferry have in various instances extorted from passengers greater sums that they are legally entitled to … the occupiers of the said ferry have in many instances been guilty of neglect and delay in carrying passengers over the said ferry and that the boats are dangerous and much out of repair … Resolved: Carriages, Horses and passengers in the large boat two shillings and six pence per wheel for carriages, two pence for a man and horse, one penny for every passenger be continued and when any passenger shall demand the small boat that six pence be paid by each passenger for such conveyance.
> [UWB/BP 3452b]

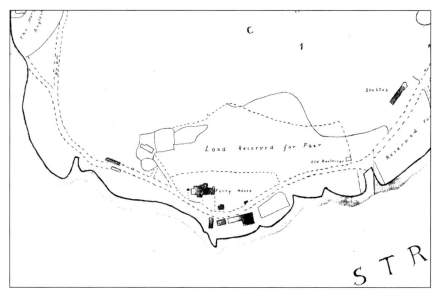

Plan of the shore at Menai Bridge showing the Ferry House.

The Cambria Inn, Menai Bridge. This was previously known as the Ferry House and the Three Tuns. In 1687, a man named Conningsby Williams applied for a licence to build a house for ferrymen 'upon the waste called Porthaethwy Common.' [Colin Ryan]

Such impositions as far as the travelling public was concerned continued until the Menai Bridge was opened in 1826. The Porthaethwy ferry then ceased to function. People wishing to cross the strait were no longer bound by the idiosyncratic ways of the ferrymen and the dangers associated with the crossing.

In 1820 Miss Jane Silence Williams, a descendent of the two brothers John and Hugh Williams who held an interest in the ferry from 1594 and Holland Williams her uncle who in 1795 bought out the Crown's interest in the rents of the ferry, was awarded the sum of £26,394-7s-6d by a Sheriff's jury at Beaumaris by way of compensation for loss of earnings once the ferry had become redundant. [UWB BP3465] As she was a minor at the time of the award, the money was held in trust until she became of age which coincided with her marriage to Sir David Erskine.

4: Moel-y-Don Ferry

ALTHOUGH VERY LITTLE IS KNOWN OF THE ORIGIN OF THE LLANIDAN FERRY, a brief reference in the Sheriff's Account of 1298 at least confirms its existence. On a 1750 map of the Menai Strait, a field near Llanidan in Anglesey, bearing the name of Pant-yr-Yscraphie (Hollow of the Ferryboat), is further evidence that a ferry crossed from this vicinity to a point below Llanfairisgaer church on the mainland, from where a track led inland. Possibly as the result of silting and the resultant sandbank creating a hazard, the ferry was moved to a point on the Anglesey shore, opposite Felinheli at Moel-y-Don. During the Tudor period, the Crown ferries of Moel-y-Don and Tal-y-Foel were leased out as a single undertaking and, although they provided a small but regular income, Charles I decided in 1629 to sell his Moel-y-Don and Tal-y-Foel ferry rights 'for a substantial sum of money' against long leases, as part of a programme of selling Crown assets to alleviate his financial problems.

Unlike Tal-y-Foel, the Moel-y-Don ferry was capable of transporting animals and for this reason gained a monopoly for conveying produce on horseback from Anglesey to the Caernarfon market. Although considered safer than some of the other ferries, especially Tal-y-Foel which suffered from the uncertainty of wind and tide, accidents did occur on the Moel-y-Don from time to time. A letter written on 12 December 1710 described one such incident: 'Bollodon [Moel-y-Don] Ferry Boat sunk with 15 men and 10 horses in her, 'twas to their good luck they were near the shore on Carnarvonshire side'.

Eighteenth-century documents relating to the local ferries produced a variation of spellings as shown on the following extract from a lease:

Moel-y-Don Ferry, the view of Felinheli from the Anglesey shore. The ferry slipway can be seen left of centre. [AC]

ferry Talvoyle between Penmaen and Llanthoyn [Llanddwyn] for 24 years and a half from 30 May 1770 at a rent of 41 shillings and for the ferry Llanden [Llaniden] otherwise Bonidon [Moel-y-Don] yearly rent of 21 shillings for the ferry Talvoyle [Tal-y-Foel]. 1796 Draft Memorial of Lord Boston re ferry Llanden otherwise Bonyden between Penmaen and Llanthoyn. [UB Lligwy Papers 1047]

Moel-y-Don Ferry, the view from Felinheli. The ferry slipway can be seen on the left with the Cutter Inn right of centre. [AC]

Another variation, 'Bon y Dom' (bottom of the mound), which appeared on official eighteenth-century documents, may be a reference to Dinas, a small hamlet between Llanfairisgaer church and the (Felinheli) village. The Moel-y-Don crossing, being shorter and safer than that at Tal-y-Foel, proved to be popular and consequently profitable. Its ferry position was well chosen, especially when Felinheli developed as an outlet for slates from the expanding Dinorwic quarry at Llanberis.

A right of way claimed by Lord Uxbridge of Plas Newydd to pass over Faenol land had been a contentious issue with its owners for many years. A letter dated 19 May 1792, written by Thomas Wright, refers to the Moel-y-Don ferry:

I have been informed that the Plas Newydd family held the Moelydon Ferry under Lord Boston's ancestors for many years and the late Sir N. Bayly having the command of the Ferrymen ordered the boat down to Plas Newydd when he wanted to go either to or from thence whenever the road through Vaynol was passable which I should think he had no legal right to do so as it deprived the public of the boats whilst he was passing and in all probability his having the command of the ferry boats was the reason why he went through Vaynol farm to the Bangor road as it was so much nearer than going to Moelydon or Borth and no one living in Vaynol who would give offence by preventing him. Lord Uxbridge I believe does not rent the ferry and if he has no right to order the ferry boat down to Plas Newydd he can have no right of a road through Vaynol. [GAS Vaynol 2562]

Above and left, two views of the Cutter Inn at Moel-y-Don Ferry [GAS & AC]

The ferryboat Conway *awaiting passengers at Port Dinorwic [AC]*

In 1817, the Board of Commissioners of HM Woods and Forests and Land Revenue recommended that a lease covering both the Tal-y-Foel and Moel-y-Don ferries be granted to Lord Boston for 31 years at a rent of £13-6s-0d for the former and £26-12s-0d for the latter. Nevertheless, Boston continued to pay the former rents of 21s and 41s respectively until a new lease, dated 30 January 1823, was granted for 31 years at a combined rent of £39-18s-0d.

An advertisement in the *North Wales Chronicle* of 11 October 1827 referred to the Moel-y-Don Ferry being 'let to the highest bidder for one year at the house of John Jones, Innholder, called Garddfon [Felinheli], … on Saturday 13 of October instant.' In 1852 the ferry lease was held by one John Owen.

Harry Williams, licensee of the Ty'n-y-Borth Inn at Moel-y-Don, a popular place to wait for the ferry. This inn had previously been known as the Cutter Inn. [GAS]

A letter published in the *Caernarvon & Denbigh Herald* in 1893 referred to purported, and possibly exaggerated, problems being experienced with the Moel-y-Don ferry service.

> It is well known that the ferriage across the Menai Straits from Carnarvonshire to Anglesey is different and occasionally indifferent ranging from the superior service at Garth to the antiquated accommodation at Moelydon by Port Dinorwic ... The boats are semi coracles and leaky. There is a rude stone jetty on the Anglesey side. But what about the accommodation or waiting passengers especially on boisterous weather? On the Carnarvonshire side there is – and temperance people may take a lesson from it – a licensed place where people may take shelter. But in Mona there is only a bleak shore with a rustic public house looming in the distance. I could not recommend a more useful business for the Anglesey Temperance Association than to spend some of the money which it collects upon making shelters on the Anglesey side of Moelydon where hundreds of Llanberis quarrymen cross.

A man named John Williams became the leaseholder in 1874 and he held it for a period of 21 years at a rent of £37 *per annum*, undertaking to maintain four ferryboats, two for use by passengers and two for the conveying of 'horses, sheep, cattle, carriages, merchandise, goods and produce'. He also had to provide a signal bell on each side of the strait as well as displaying the tolls payable. Three years later, John Williams sub-let the lease to Richard Williams who held it until it was taken over by William Owen in 1897, by which time the rent had risen to £47 *per annum* due to the expenditure incurred in extending the jetties or piers.

Anglesey men who worked at the Dinorwic quarry, had to endure living in barracks near their place of work from Monday to Saturday. They welcomed the opportunity of returning home for the weekend. After the train journey from Llanberis to Penscoins at

Dinorwic quarrymen aboard the ferry for the crossing from Felinheli to Moel-y-Don. [Len Williams]

Port Dinorwic, they would board the first available ferryboat. After the short weekend break at home, they set off early on the Monday morning from various villages, often arriving wet, cold and tired for the ferry crossing. In addition to the quarrymen boarding the boat at Moel-y-Don, the ferryman was quite willing to deviate to pick up others at Trefarthin or Porthamal on the Anglesey shore, for an additional penny or two, in order to save the quarrymen the extra walk, especially during the winter.

With so many waiting to cross the strait it was not unusual for the ferry to have as many as 40 men aboard, each carrying the ubiquitous white *walad* (sack) containing provisions for the week's stay in the barracks. Unless the ferryboat had the benefit of a sail, between three and six of the passengers would lend a hand with the oars to expedite the journey across the water.

Captain William Williams leased the ferry from 1912 until 1920 at a rental of £47 *per annum*. During the First World War when he commanded a mine-sweeper and later the SS *Snowdon*, Williams sublet the lease to Captain Thomas Lillie and Harry Jones Roberts who were assisted from time to time by Robert Caddock and Thomas Henry Williams (Vaults Bach). Lillie took over the lease when it expired in 1920. The gross revenue was stated to be approximately £400 but, as the result of the income having fallen to £70 by 1935, the rent was reduced to £5 *per annum*.

The three boats involved during the 1920s and 1930s were the *Conway*, *Great Orme* and the 28-foot *Menai,* the first motorised ferryboat to be used at Moel-y-Don. Thomas

Lillie also held two in reserve: a 28-foot ferryboat called *Betty* (built by Matthew Owen at Menai Bridge) and *Nancy*.

The newly introduced bus services that operated in Anglesey from the 1920s, initially from the Newborough area, proved to be very popular with the quarrymen as they provided an alternative to the long walk to and from the ferry. To encourage a regular clientele the quarrymen were charged 7/- per week for the bus journey to Llanberis. Although the original buses were very basic and unreliable by today's standard, they provided a variety of routes. As a result of this, the role of the ferries, which were affected by bad weather and tides, gradually diminished. When discussions between Crown Lands and Caernarvonshire County Council began in 1930 regarding the future of the Moel-y-Don ferry, a member of the Llanfairisgaer Parish Council made the observation: 'as a business proposition I would not accept it as a gift – traffic between October–May practically nil, and summer months Port Dinorwic people crossing to the Anglesey sands i.e. very few'. [GAS XC2/6/123] When Captain Lillie gave up the ferry lease on 10 October 1935, a letter from the Crown Receiver stated: 'very few people made use of it [the ferry] as they prefer to use the buses. Up to the present no person has been found to take up a new lease'.

As a result of a Parliamentary Act of 1919, which enabled local authorities to acquire the right to operate existing ferries, minutes of the joint meeting of the Anglesey and Caernarvonshire County Councils on 3 August 1936 revealed that Crown Lands were prepared to sell the rights to the Moel-y-Don ferry to the joint councils for £50. The councils, having accepted the offer, tendered for a ferry boat suitable for transporting twelve passengers. Those that were submitted included: Dickie & Son Ltd supplying a new boat and dinghy for £260; Morris & Leavett £175 (plus £15 for a dinghy) and Matthew Owen & Son £142 (plus £15 for a dinghy). The latter tender was accepted and the Alliance Assurance Yacht & Motor Boat proposal form, dated 25 April 1938, revealed that the 20ft x 7ft x 3ft 3ins clencher-built boat was to be fitted with

Moel-y-Don jetty and ticket office. [Len Williams]

The Moel-y-Don ferry jetty and ticket office, Felinheli. [Len Williams]

a 7-horsepower Kelvin engine and a few other embellishments at a cost of £195, and that the boat was to be named *Arvona*. Shortly afterwards, Arthur Roberts was appointed as the ferryman at a wage of £1-10s-0d per week. At the outbreak of war in 1939 the *Arvona* was allocated the number 103 and authorised by the Resident Naval Officer at Caernarfon to be used until 22.00 hrs – lights could not be used under any circumstance. [GAS XC2/6/210, XD1-809] The cost of crossing by ferry in June 1938 was: adults 2d single and 3d return; children 1d; workmen's weekly tickets 1s (for use between Monday and Saturday only). Individuals taking perambulators and bicycles on the ferry were charged 2d per item. [GAS XC 2/6/210] When animals were being transported the charges were: horses, cow or bullock 1s each, calves, pigs 3d each, sheep, lambs, goats, dogs 2d each. The weekly service timetable was given as: Port Dinorwic 6.35 a.m., Moel-y-Don 6.45 a.m., Port Dinorwic 8.20 a.m., Moel-y-Don 8.30 a.m., then half hourly until the last boat left Port Dinorwic at 7.50 p.m. and Moel-y-Don at 8 p.m. On Sundays the service commenced from Port Dinorwic at 7.50 a.m. and Moel-y-Don at 8 a.m. then a two-hourly service until the last boat left Port Dinorwic at 3.50 p.m. and Moel-y-Don at 4 p.m.

The Moel-y-Don ferryman, Edward Owen, 1958. [Keith Morris]

By the 1930s, due to the increasing number of cars on the roads, consideration had been given to the transporting of vehicles across on a specially adapted ferry but this notion was rejected by the Crown Commissioners.

When the *Arvona's* engine required an overhaul in December 1941 the joint county

ANGLESEY AND CAERNARVONSHIRE COUNTY COUNCILS.

MOEL-Y-DON FERRY.

REGULATIONS

Made by the Anglesey and Caernarvonshire County Councils pursuant to the Ferries (Acquisition by Local Authorities) Act, 1919.

1. No person shall, after any ferry boat commences to leave any landing stage or beach used in connection therewith, board or attempt to board such ferry boat.

2. No person being carried on board any ferry boat, shall attempt to leave the same until such ferry boat has ceased to be in motion, and has reached and been properly secured to one of the ferry landing stages.

3. No person shall embark on or disembark from any ferry boat except by walking on or through the gangways provided for such purpose.

4. No vessel, craft, raft, timber, or other things shall lie at, or be placed, made fast or moored at, or be allowed to drift near or in the way of any of the landing stages or beaches of the ferry so as to be an obstruction thereto, or so as to prevent the free transit of any of the ferry boats to and from any landing stage or beach.

5. No person, except the Council's servants, duly authorized shall touch or interfere with any engine on board the ferry boat, or enter any part of the Councils' premises not intended or set apart for the use of passengers.

6. Every person in charge of any vehicle, shall place such vehicle, according to the directions of the Councils' servants, and in the case of any vehicle when on board the ferry boat shall properly secure such vehicle ; and in passing over any of the landing stages or beaches shall drive such vehicles with all proper care and at a safe pace.

7. No person shall take or attempt to take on board any ferry boat used for vehicles, without the permission first asked for and obtained from the Ferry Manager or other official for the time being in charge of the ferry, any vehicle, which with its load and the persons accompanying the same, exceeds the weight of two and a half hundredweights ($2\frac{1}{2}$ cwts), or which, with its load, exceeds the length of six fee out.).

8. Every person using the said ferry shall, whilst on board any ferry boat, or at any of the landing stages or beaches, conform in all respects to the orders and directions of the servants of the Councils in charge of the ferry boats, landing stages, or beaches for the regulation of the traffic therein and thereon, and for the prevention of crowding and accidents.

9. No person shall enter upon, or use, or attempt to use, any of the ferry boats, landing stages, waiting rooms or premises whilst in a state of drunkenness and on that account likely to constitute a source of danger.

10. The officers and servants of the Councils in charge of the said ferry boat, landing stages, and premises, or any of them, may refuse to receive upon any landing stage or beach, or on board any ferry boat, any person who, by reason of drunkeness or otherwise, is in such a state, or misconducts himself or herself in such a manner as to constitute, or be likely to constitute, a source of danger ; and if any person is in such a state or so misconducts himself or herself as aforesaid, on board any ferry boat, the said officers or servants or any of them may put him or her on shore at any convenient place.

11. No persons (except Members of His Majesty's Forces when on duty) shall take any loaded fire-arms into, place, or leave any loaded fire-arms on board any of the ferry boats, or at or in any of the beaches, landing stages, waiting rooms, or any premises of the Councils used in connection with the ferry or in or on any of the offices and approaches connected and held therewith.

12. No person shall drop or throw down on or in the ferry boats any lighted matches, cigarettes, cigars, tobacco or other burning material.

13. Every person in anywise offending against or contravening any of the preceding regulations shall, for every such offence be liable on summary conviction to pay a penalty not exceeding forty shillings for each offence.

14. These regulations shall come into operation and take effect on the expiration of fourteen days after the date of the confirmation thereof by the Minister of Transport.

Dated this 13th day of December, 1938.

The Common Seal of the County Council of the Administrative }
County of Anglesey was hereunto affixed in the presence }
of :— } (L.S.)

G. Ll. WILLIAMS,

JOHN ROBERTS.

Two members of the Council.

WALTER O. JONES,
Clerk of the Council.

The Common Seal of the County Council of the Administrative }
County of Caernarvon was hereunto affixed in the presence }
of :— } (L.S.)

H. ROBERTS.

W. E. WEBSTER.

Two members of the Council having the custody of the Keys of the Seal of the Council.

DAVID G. JONES.
Clerk of the Council.

The Minister of Transport hereby confirms the foregoing Regulations.
Signed on behalf of the Minister of Transport this fifth day of January, 1939.

(Signed) SIDNEY J. PAGE,
Assistant Secretary.

The Moel-y-Don ferry regulations. [AC]

The Moel-y-Don ferry passengers being rowed across on a windless day, c.1910. [GAS]

*The Moel-y-Don ferry
boat* Ellen, *c.1910.
[Len Williams]*

councils decided to buy a 23ft x 8ft 2ins x 2ft 11ins boat with a 6/8hp Kelvin engine for £75 from Tom Lillie, the retired ferryman. Eight years later, Charles Pearson (Hull) Ltd supplied a new ferryboat (20ft x 7ft 6ins x 3ft draught) powered by a Thornycroft Handy Billy DB2.7/9hp petrol/paraffin model engine, with reverse gear costing £541 and suitable for carrying 12 passengers. [GAS XC2/5/92]

Arthur Roberts was succeeded as ferryman in August 1941 by Herman Karl Petroll who carried out the duties of ferryman until an illness in July 1945 forced him to resign from the post. He was succeeded by Edward Owen, who had served as a chief petty

Porthaethwy Ferry by J. Warwick Smith (1749–1831). The figure in the foreground is standing on the Caernarfonshire shore, close to the site of the George Hotel. The rock in the middle of the strait is Ynys-y-Moch, on which Telford later built one of the towers of his suspension bridge. The two-storey building on the far bank is the Ferry House (Cambrian Inn) at Porthaethwy. [UB]

'Embarkation of the Princess Victoria' by Joseph Butler. The 13-year-old princess and her mother, the Duchess of Kent, about to embark on a paddle steamer, possibly the PS Menai owned by Mr Thomas Assheton Smith of Vaynol, for an excursion to Conwy, August 1832.
[North-East Lincolnshire Museum Service]

The George Hotel, c.1842 The Porthaethey ferry landing stage can be seen lower right.

Ground plan of the George Hotel showing the old Holyhead Road along the shoreline, giving access to the ferry landing stage. [BU]

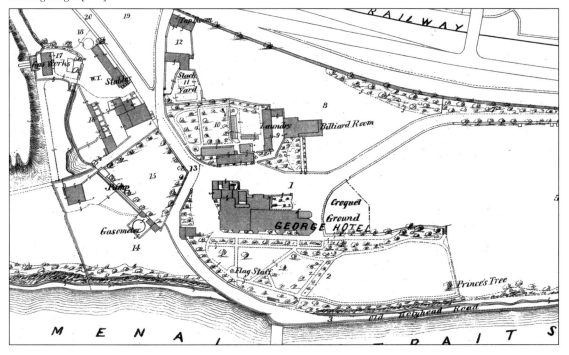

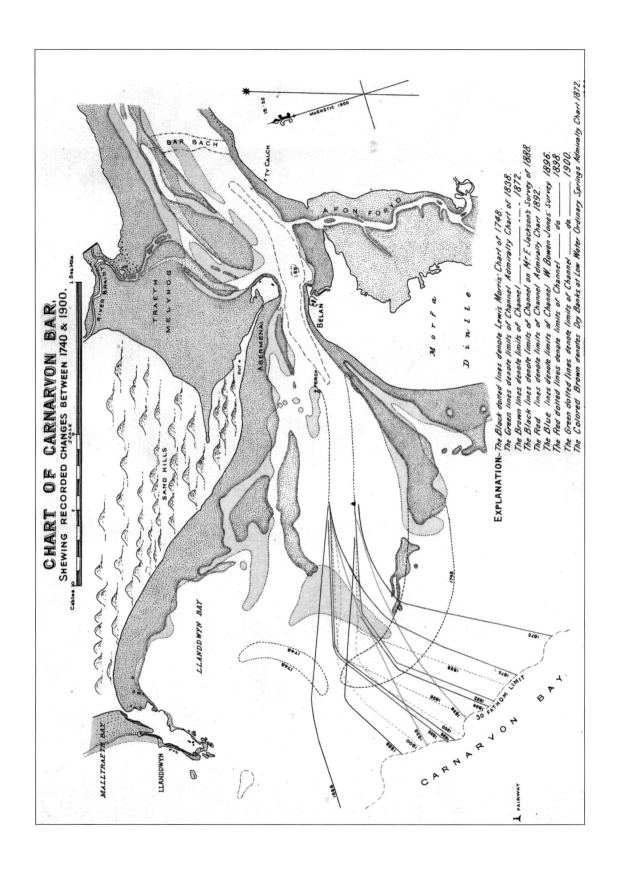

CHART OF CARNARVON BAR,

SHEWING RECORDED CHANGES BETWEEN 1740 & 1900.

Cables   SCALE   1 Sea Mile.

EXPLANATION.—The Black dotted lines denote Lewis Morris' Chart of 1748.
The Green lines denote limits of Channel Admiralty Chart of 1838.
The Brown lines denote limits of Channel ———— ———— 1872.
The Black lines denote limits of Channel on Mr F. Jackson's Survey of 1888.
The Red lines denote limits of Channel Admiralty Chart 1892.
The Blue lines denote limits of Channel W. Bowen Jones' Survey 1896.
The Red dotted lines denote limits of Channel   do.   1898.
The Green dotted lines denote limits of Channel   do.   1900.
The Colored Brown denotes Dry Banks at Low Water Ordinary Springs Admiralty Chart 1872.

BAR BACH

TY CALCH

AFON FORYD

Morfa Dinlle

BELAN

PERCH

TRAETH MELYNOG

ABERMENAI

HUT

RIVER BRAINT

SAND HILLS

LLANDDWYN BAY

MALLTRAETH BAY

LLANDDWYN

CARNARVON BAY

30 FATHOM LIMIT

FAIRWAY

MAGNETIC 1900
18°20'

Facing: Chart of the Caernarvon Bar, showing the recorded changes in the sandbanks (between 1740 and 1900), which always created problems for the operators of the Tal-y-Foel ferry. [GAS]

Above: The Menai Strait c.1855, lithograph by Thomas Picken, showing the Menai Bridge and the newly completed Britannia Bridge. In the centre foreground the Caernarfonshire landing stage of the Porthaethwy ferry can be seen just below the George Hotel. Note Vaynol Hall in the far left distance. The Marquess of Anglesey's column can be seen upper right. The paddle steamer may be the Menai, which belonged to Mr Assheton-Smith. [SM]

The stone support towers of the Britannia Bridge under construction, 1848. Lithograph by Day & Son after S. Russell. [SM]

The iron tubes of the Britannia Bridge under construction on the Caernarfonshire shore. [SM]

The Britannia Tubular and Menai Suspension bridges. Lithograph by G. Hawkins, c.1855. [SM]

The completed Britannia Bridge, c.1860. Watercolour, artist unknown. [SM]

THE BRITANNIA TUBULAR BRIDGE
MENAI STRAITS
by Norman Wilkinson R.I.

LMS

The train which left Euston on August 1st, 1848, was called The Irish Mail, and has been so named ever since. It started at 8-45 p.m. that night, and that is its time today. But the Britannia Bridge was not yet built and passengers and mail bags had to take coach from Bangor by Telford's Suspension Bridge to Anglesey where another train awaited them.

By June, 1850 the Britannia Bridge was opened to traffic, and today Robert Stephenson's mighty engineering feat stands as a memorial to the consummate skill of the Victorian generation of engineers. Today the Irish Mail provides a day and night service to Ireland, covering the journey between Euston and Kingstown (Dun Laoghaire) in a little over 9 hours.

Above: An iconic poster for the London, Midland & Scottish Railway, featuring the Britannia Bridge by the artist Sir Norman Wilkinson (1878–1971). [SM]

David Pritchard, 'Dafydd r'Abar', who operated the Aber ferry at Caernarfon prior to the construction of the Aber bridge.

The blazing Britannia Bridge illuminates the nightscape on 23 May 1970. [AC]

One of the steel arch sections for the Britannia Bridge ready for towing from Port Dinorwic. [AC]

Dismantling the fire-damaged tubes on the Britannia Bridge.

Left: To enable the tubes to be removed, a bogie carriage with a hydraulic jacking system on board was moved into position within the tube by a diesel locomotive. With the section supported by jacks, it was then cut free from the base by oxyacetylene cutters. [AC]

Below: The locomotive reversed to a position where a crane could lift the cut section off the bogie to the ground, where it was cut into smaller pieces. [AC]

Facing page.
Top: Once the east–west tube had been entirely removed, a pre-cast concrete railway track bed was put in place. On completion, the same procedure was repeated for the second tube that had carried the west-east railway track. [AC]

Below: On completion of the railway tracks, a new road deck was constructed above them to take the A5 (later the A55) over the Menai Strait. [AC]

The completed reconstructed Britannia Bridge showing the new steel arches, the railway deck and the roadway in place. *[AC]*

Facing page: London, Midland & Scottish Railway poster advertising the daily sailings of the St Tudno III *and* St Seiriol *from Liverpool to Llandudno and Menai Bridge. [UB]*

LIVERPOOL & NORTH WALES

"ST. TUDNO" or "ST. SEIRIOL"

May to September

for Llandudno and Menai Bridge

Leaving LIVERPOOL 10-45 a.m. due back about 7-30 p.m.
LIVERPOOL and LLANDUDNO in 2 hours.

For particulars apply The Liverpool & North Wales Steamship Co., Ltd., 40, Chapel Street, Liverpool

CONVENIENT LMS TRAINS LEAVE THIS STATION
IN CONNECTION WITH THESE SAILINGS

LMS

MV St Trillo II *off Llandudno, c.1950. [Colin Evans]*

A tranquil scene at the Moel-y-Don ferry jetty and inn today. [AC]

officer in the Royal Navy during the war. In addition to a wage of £4, paid by the joint councils, Owen was allowed to retain the current fares but, out of this meagre income, had to pay the running-costs of the ferry boat. Other local names that operated the Moel-y-Don ferry were: Sidney Chubb, Ben Dop, Hugh Dop and Eric Owen. [GAS XC2/6/233]

Even though the ferry continued to be used for recreational purposes and by people living in the Moel-y-Don area wishing to visit the numerous shops available in Port Dinorwic, the Caernarfonshire and Anglesey County Councils decided in 1958 that, because of the diminishing number of passengers using the ferry, it was no longer economically viable to continue with the service, even during the summer months. Various attempts were made to continue the ferry by providing a private service but the availability of other forms of transport ensured its demise in 1962 although a ferry boat was spasmodically operated for a short period on an unofficial basis.

Ferryman Eric Owen
[AC]

Passengers awaiting the
ferry at Moel-y-Don, in
the 1950s.
[Len Williams]

5: Caernarfon Harbour & Ferries

Caernarfon Harbour

UNTIL THE END OF THE EIGHTEENTH CENTURY Caernarfon harbour was in a deplorable state, particularly as far as quayside storage facilities and the means of loading or unloading vessels were concerned. In an attempt to improve the situation an order was made by Caernarfon Corporation in February 1730 that 'henceforth no slates shall be unloaded or put down at or upon any part of the ground shore or land under or near to the castle of Carnarvon except on payment of halfpenny per 1,000'. [GAS XD88-4-170]

On the 17 June 1793, an Act for 'enlarging, deepening, cleansing, improving and regulating the harbour of Carnarvon' was passed, the preamble of which stated:

Whereas the harbour of Carnarvon … been greatly choaked [sic] and filled up with mud, sand and dirt and vessels of burthen are thereby prevented from getting up to the quays, wharfs and landing places within the harbour and the shipping lying in the said harbour are exposed to inconvenience and danger: And whereas the quays and piers already made and constructed within the said harbour are not sufficient for the preservation thereof and the reception and convenient lying of the ships and vessels resorting thereto and for the requisite and convenient despatch in loading and unloading it would be of great benefit and advantage to the merchants and others living in or trading to and from the town and port of Carnarvon … were properly enlarged, deepened, cleansed, improved and regulated and if new and additional piers and quays were constructed and built for the preservation of the harbour and the accommodation of the trade thereof.

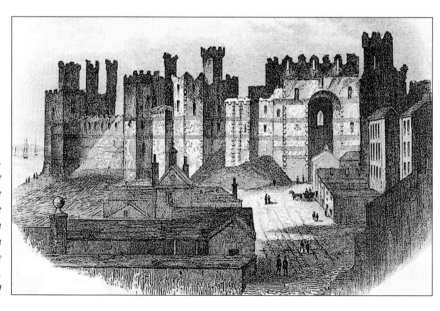

Caernarfon Castle, viewed 'from the terrace' before the construction of the slate quay and harbour. An engraving based on a deguereotype taken by W.L. Sharp of Rhyl. [Keith Morris]

A letter of 3 March 1815, addressed to Lord Anglesey, mentioned *inter alia* that there was a need to improve the Castle Square, or Green as it was then called, and use the spoil from such work to improve the harbour:

> ... a Plan has been suggested to the Trustees of the Harbour, to lower about 5 feet of the surface of the Castle Green (known as Maes Glas), which would bring it upon a level with the road from the Goat Inn to Nelson Street & to carry that soil down to assist in filling up the New Quay and to continue a road from the Bridge across the Castle green down to the New Quay. [UCNW-PN 2058]

Another account, which appears to confirm that it was the intention of the town dignitaries to improve and extend the quay, stated:

> the huge mound of earth was removed about the year 1817 ... (the corporation) employed the poor ... in removing the earth and wheeling it down to improve the quay, which had been erected c1803 – has lately been extended. The quay wall had been built against piles and the rubbish taken from the green thrown behind and levelled ... The Castle Hotel was built in 1834 and the Post Office opened in the square in 1880.

A similar resolution was made in 1817 by the Carnarvon Harbour Trust to 'level a piece of ground opposite Castle Green the property of the corporation for the purpose of completing and improving the quay.'

Subsequent to the additional improvements carried out as the result of the 1844 Act, a survey was made of the harbour in January of the following year which revealed that the new pier head was nearly completed and that 'the rebuilding of the quay wall within the harbour will be finished in the course of the present week.' [GAS XD88-4-57, 59]

Further to the enactment in 1877 of a parliamentary bill for the improvement of the harbour, a report in a local paper of the Harbour Trust's recent activities stated:

> in view of the advantages that will accrue to the Trust by the extension of the Narrow Gauge Railway to Caernarvon Harbour and the construction of the quays (it was suggested) that the Harbour Trust contribute £1,000 towards the cost of the new quays to be built by the Railway Company on the property of the Trustees ... and further that the Harbour Trustees undertake to open and close the bridge proposed to be made across the Harbour by the Railway Company. [C&DH, 10.2.1888]

A further report regarding the extension added:

> Narrow Gauge – Railway Extension – on the southern side of the Seiont, the Narrow Gauge Railway Company propose to make wharves from which to load on ship-board the slate brought down from the districts served by the line; these wharves will be upon land which is now to be property of the Trust (at present slates are transferred from narrow gauge to main line trucks at Dinas). [C&DH, 2.3.1888]

Coed Helen ferry.
[Keith Morris]

Further major improvements of the harbour generally were under discussion during the 1890s and a letter to the Caernarvon Harbour Trust (dated 18 December 1896) stated that an application was to be submitted 'for an Act to confer powers for the Corporation of Caernarvon in relation to the ferry between Caernarvon and Anglesea, the construction of a pier and works for the purposes thereof, and for the construction of a swing bridge (commencing opposite the Eagle Tower of Carnarvon castle and terminating opposite the Aber Ferry house) over the river Seiont, also widening of the road along the coast in Llanfaglan. [GAS XM 5976/49; XD15/20/6-20/8]

The Act was passed on 15 July 1897 and work on the construction of the swing bridge was carried out between then and 1900.

Aber Ferry

In the period prior to the ferry (which ran across the river Seiont from below the castle walls) being replaced by a bridge, it was operated by David Pritchard (1808–84), or 'Dafydd R'Abar' as he was known locally, with his son, David Charles Pritchard, acting as his assistant. The fare for crossing the river by ferry was one halfpenny per person. No additional charge was made for the return journey. It recorded that 'there are special arrangements arrived at for people who cross often to pay a lower rate'.

James Menzies of Menai Bank, Caernarfon, an associated member of the Institution of Civil Engineers, wrote:

> When I first remembered the ferry it was worked by a fully able-bodied man who sculled a substantial and commodious boat capable of holding a considerable number of passengers in safety. Later the lessee became proprietor of small rowing boats for ferry work and often they were rowed by small boys. These boats would only hold

Local Volunteers assembled on the quayside awaiting to board the ferry that will take them to the Coed Helen army camp, c.1890. [AC]

ML Seabird, *approaching Caernarfon* c.*1940.* *[R. Bonner Pritchard]*

a few passengers and were very unsteady and they were only fit for being used by more or less expert men when in fine weather and occupants would necessarily have to sit down in the boats and be very careful in rising from their seats in coming to or leaving the boats otherwise they would be capsized.

The Pritchard family also ran motor launch trips along the strait and to Abermenai, a very popular destination in the 1950s (usually on Sundays), using either the *White Heather* or *Seabird*.

Aber Ferry Bridge

The Aber ferry, or Coed Helen ferry as it was also known, was replaced by a bridge in 1900. The main swing span was 156-feet and there were two adjacent fixed spans of 47-feet which provided a clear waterway 85-feet wide, sufficient for the passage of vessels in and out of the harbour. Power for the opening and shutting of the main span, as well as night-time illumination, was provided by a gas engine. As a result of the ferry no longer being required, the owner received the substantial sum of £7,000 (£400,000 at today's values) as compensation for his loss of earnings.

Caernarfon Ferry Bridge. [Richard Jones]

Anglesey Ferries

Historically, travellers heading for Anglesey from Llŷn and the south may well have crossed the 320-yard-wide channel, separating the present-day Fort Belan on the mainland and Abermenai on Anglesey, by ferry. From there they used a public carriageway which would have taken them across sand and mud a distance of some three miles to Newborough and then to Aberffraw and beyond.

Unlike other Crown ferries along the strait, Abermenai (or South Crook as it was known during the reign of Edward I) had the benefit of a ferry house. It also had the advantage of operating under 'ideal conditions as it was sheltered from north, south and west winds'. Even so, in 1664, the ferry boat capsized within a few yards of the shore and 79 passengers were drowned.

Compared to the Abermenai ferry, which was valued at £7 per annum in 1608, the nearby Tal-y-Foel ferry was valued at £11, the Moel-y-Don at £5 and the Porthaethwy at £25. Later that century, the Beaumaris ferry, which was maintained and equipped by the corporation, was let at £8 per annum.

By 1711, there were two boats operating at Abermenai and it was decided that a new one was required which would cost £50, twice as much as that paid for the largest boat at Beaumaris at that time. In 1719, the Abermenai ferry was leased to Lord Bulkeley for 31 years at a rent of £4-10s-0d, on condition that he rebuilt the ferry-house and provided 'good and sufficient boats'. When Lord Bulkeley petitioned for a renewal of the lease in 1741, the ferry was reported by the Surveyor General for the Crown as:

> having a ferry house and two boats kept … for Carriage of Horses laden from Anglesea to the Market town of Carnarvon and from South Wales to Holyhead in the way to Ireland …. I find that the Ferry house which was in ruins at the time of granting the last Lease has since been rebuilt by the said Lord Bulkeley.

In 1771, road guides advised people travelling to Holyhead from Caernarfon to take the 'Abermeney Ferry' and then proceed to their destination via Newborough, Aberffraw and Bodedern. By 1799, travellers were being directed to Bangor Ferry and then, in 1808, to the Moel-y-Don ferry. As soon as the Menai Bridge was opened in 1826, travellers were directed to cross the strait at that point. Gradually, however, the number of passengers using the Tal-y-Foel to Caernarfon ferry increased due to it being more accessible to people living in the vicinity of Newborough when compared to Abermenai, where passenger numbers dwindled to such an extent that the ferryman, Shôn Williams, eventually had to resort to parish relief. When the Tal-y-Foel ferry was sold to the Caernarfon Corporation in 1874, the rights to the Abermenai ferry were also included. Official documents described the ferry as:

> The King's ancient ferry … to and from Tan y Foel for carrying persons, carriages, horses and cattle … persons on foot two pence and for each person on horseback three pence for every score of sheep seven pence and for all other cattle two pence by the head.

Periodic complaints had been made about the Tal-y-Foel ferry service including:

Aber Menai Ferry,
c.1840. [Keith Morris]

It was reported that there was general dissatisfaction with the Tal y Foel ferry. People were kept waiting to get across, the boatmen were insolent to ladies and the boats were dirty owing to pigs being carried in the same boat as passengers.

In 1817, possibly as the result of the poor service that was being provided by the ferry, the brothers David and William Williams, who lived in a small house below Plas Brereton, Caernarfon began to carry passengers in their boat from near their home to Barras on the Anglesey shore. They were asked to stop this unauthorised service by the Commissioners of Woods and Forests but to no avail. Due to the expertise of their solicitor, John Evans of Porth-yr-Aur, Caernarfon, not only were they discharged without having to account to Lord Boston for the profit they had made, they were also spared the costs of the court proceedings. Three years later, the ferry was still being operated illegally by the two brothers when the boat capsized with 23 passengers on board. William Williams was amongst those who drowned and only one person, Hugh Williams of Bodowyr Brynsiencyn, was saved. A total of £603 was collected for the benefit of the bereaved families, most of whom were from the parish of Llanidan. Even though his brother had died as a result of the accident, David Williams persisted with the ferry and consequently was gaoled for six weeks but was quickly released as the result of a local petition on his behalf.

The Abermenai ferry service ceased to operate in the middle of the nineteenth century and by 1872 the ferry house is shown on an Admiralty chart as a ruin (although a Caernarvon Harbour Trust account dated July 1873 refers to 'whitewashing house at Abermenai'). [GAS XD88-4-7]

PS *Paul Pry*

The *Paul Pry*, built for the Wye Steam Boat Co, was launched in November 1827 with George Pearce as master. She was used to convey passengers from Hereford to Chepstow at a cost of ten shillings. The following year, the vessel departed for the Menai Strait where she was intended to be used as a tender by the St George Steam Packet Company which operated the *Prince Llewelyn* and *Snowdon* amongst other vessels.

The *Paul Pry's* intended role appears to have changed by the early 1830s when the vessel began competing with the ferry authorised by Lord Boston in a ten-year lease granted in December 1830. Within a short time, the *Paul Pry* had made a profit of £400 by 'carrying passengers, goods, horses &c from Caernarvon to Barras ... all to the injury and detriment of Lord Boston's lessees'. Unfortunately, when the case was tried at the Assizes, it was decided that the Caernarvon–Barras route did not lie within the limits of the ferries described in the 1830 lease and further action against the owners of the *Paul Pry* was thought to be futile. [BU Lligwy Papers 14]

The *North Wales Chronicle* 10 April 1832 described the scene when the vessel first arrived at Caernarfon:

> On Thursday afternoon the *Paul Pry* arrived at Carnarvon bedizened with flags and streamers from stem to stern. She was received with a salute of artillery from the Corporation guns and those belonging to Mr Parry on the Twthill ... The crier was next sent through the town to invite all who chose to make a trip to Anglesey gratis to embark in the Paul Pry at six on Friday evening. She started at six accordingly with a pretty large cargo of live lumber on board and after repeatedly grounding on the sand banks, returned to Carnarvon a little before midnight most of her passengers having contrived during the voyage to catch colds and sore throats for the benefit of their medical advisers. We are sorry to learn that the engineer had two of his fingers chopped off and a third much injured while attending to the machinery.

CARNARVON, MENAI BRIDGE, BANGOR AND BEAUMARIS.

THE NEW STEAM PACKET,

PAUL PRY,

Of 20 Horse Power,

LEAVES CARNARVON EVERY MORNING (except Sundays,) commencing on the 1st of May, for the above places, taking Passengers to the Liverpool and Dublin Steamers; and will meet them at the Menai Bridge, on their return from Liverpool, to take Passengers to Carnarvon.

FARES.   Cabin   Deck

Carnarvon, to Menai Bridge & Bangor 1s.6d. 1s.0d.

———————Beaumaris 2 0 1 6

Menai Bridge & Bangor to Beaumaris 0 0 0 6

Beaumaris to Bangor 0 0 0 6

Refreshments on Board.

Passengers by this boat will enjoy a view of the most grand, romantic, and interesting scenery that can possibly be presented to the eye:—Plasnewydd the magnificent Seat of the Marquis of Anglesey; the Alpine range of the Snowdonian Mountains, the Menai Bridge, that masterpiece of human art; the unrivalled Bay of Beaumaris; Puffin Island, &c.

For further Particulars, apply to Mr. George Evans, Sportsman Hotel, Carnarvon; Mr. F. W. Hall, St. George Steam Packet Office, Bangor Ferry; and to Mr. Richard Rowlands, Castle Hotel, Bangor.

A Coach will also leave the Sportsman Hotel, every Morning, with Passengers, to meet the Liverpool Steamers.

N.B. By this arrangement the Public will not be delayed nor disappointed.

Advert for the Paul Pry, *NWC 30 April 1833. [Keith Morris]*

Tal-y-Foel – paddle steamer at the Menai Hotel. [Alun Williams]

It was stated that the *Paul Pry*, with its 16hp engine, had the advantage of only drawing 2ft 10ins of water. Nevertheless, it was stated that 'on her second trip that day she was lodged very comfortably upon a bank for some time in trying to pass through the Garth-y-Foel'. Fares for passengers were: steerage 1d, deck 2d and 3d in a 'spacious cabin'. In addition, animals were charged at: horses 6d, cattle 4d, pigs 3d and sheep 2d. The newspaper report added that 'such has been the commencement of this absurd and unjustifiable invasion of the rights of Lord Boston and his lessees'.

As the 'new' ferry service was eventually found not to be financially viable, the *Paul Pry* started operating five days a week to Bangor, Beaumaris and Conwy, connecting with the Liverpool steamers at Menai Bridge. The packet's connection with Caernarfon only lasted until May 1833 when the vessel left the area.

The Tal-y-Foel to Caernarfon ferry was considered the most difficult of the ferries to operate due to the ever-changing position of the sandbanks in the Menai Strait, some of which were quicksands, and having to negotiate the few available channels. There were also problems with reaching a point on the Anglesey side where passengers could safely disembark. Even when the point of disembarkation was moved a few yards to the north-east in 1850, the same problems remained. The weather was certainly a factor that had to be taken into consideration due to the exposed position of the crossing, particularly on those days when passengers were rowed across in open boats, only some of which had the benefit of a sail. To facilitate those passengers travelling from Tal-y-Foel to Waterloo Port, a new landing quay and ferry pier were built at the latter location towards the end of 1842 by the Caernarvon Harbour Trust. In 1870, when the new Caernarfon harbour was constructed, a slipway was provided for the use of the ferry at a cost of £1,600. [GAS XD88-4-7; XDI/ 809]

In May 1848, as a result of the disquiet being expressed in the town about the standard of the ferry service, a meeting, chaired by the Mayor of Caernarfon, decided that a company called the Menai Steam Navigation Co would become responsible for running the ferry and Lord Boston sold the ferry rights to the company for £225 (£13,000 at present-day values). John Jones, who rented the ferry at the time, received £30 compensation (£1,750 at present-day values). Two years earlier, a new boat house had been built at Tal-y-Foel. [BU Lligwy Papers 14].

Top: Tal-y-Foel paddle-steamer ferry. [AC}

Centre: Tal-y-Foel, c.1890. [AC]

Right: The remains of the Tal-y-Foel landing stage.
[GAS]

BOROUGH OF CARNARVON.

CARNARVON & ANGLESEA FERRY.

BYE-LAWS

MADE BY

The Mayor, Aldermen & Burgesses of the Borough of Carnarvon,

(hereinafter called THE CORPORATION), in pursuance of the powers and provisions of Section 12 of the Carnarvon Corporation Act, 1897, at a Meeting held on the 19th day of August, 1908, for regulating the use of the Carnarvon and Anglesea Ferry. These Bye-Laws shall come into operation on the 1st day of October, 1908.

1.—Any person who offends against any of the following Bye-laws shall be liable for each offence to a penalty not exceeding Five pounds.

2.—No person shall pass to or from any boat otherwise than through the turnstiles or gateways, or over the gangways provided for the purpose, and along the Ferry Pier or Landing Stage.

3.—No person shall embark or disembark on or from any Ferry boat otherwise than by the gangway provided for the purpose.

4.—All passengers by the boats shall pay their fares and obtain tickets at the place or places provided for the purpose, and shall when requested deliver up their tickets to the officer or officers appointed to collect the same.

5.—All passengers by the boats shall, on the termination of each trip, be landed before any other person or persons shall be allowed to embark on board such boats, and no person shall embark before such landing be completed.

6.—No person shall be in a state of intoxication, or guilty of any riotous or disorderly conduct, or use any abusive or indecent language, or beg or ask for alms on board any of the boats, or at or in or upon any of the slips, piers, landing places, pay-gates, or Ferry premises.

7.—No person shall wilfully obstruct or impede the passage to or from any of the boats.

8.—No person shall smoke tobacco in the cabins, or spit on any of the boats or Ferry premises.

9.—No person shall obstruct or hinder the superintendent, collector, masters, seamen, or servants of the Corporation, or any of them, in the due execution of his or their duty.

10.—It shall be lawful for the superintendent, master, or person in charge of any boat used in working the said Ferry, to direct any passenger or person on board such boat to occupy any such part thereof as such superintendent, master, or person in charge may think proper, and no person shall refuse or neglect to comply with such instructions.

11.—All carters or drivers of vehicles using or having used the boats, shall lead their horses along the gangways, piers, and stages, and all carts, carriages, and other vehicles with horses shall not be left on the boat, pier, or stage without a carter or driver in attendance, and such carter or driver shall place a scotch through or under the back and front wheels of the cart, carriage, or vehicle whilst on board such boat, and the carter or driver shall have charge of the horses by the bridle while crossing the Straits.

12.—A person bringing any goods, luggage, cattle, matter or thing, on board any boat used in working the said Ferry, shall comply with any order of the superintendent, master, or person in charge thereof, with respect to the placing of any such goods, luggage, cattle, matter or thing, in such part of the said boat as such superintendent, master, or person in charge of such boat, may direct.

13.—Any passenger remaining on board at the end of a trip shall pay the return fare to the master or person in charge of the boat.

14.—No person shall allow any goods, cattle, merchandise, luggage, matter or thing belonging to him or her, to remain on the boats, landing stages, slips, or other part or parts of the Ferry premises, for the space of one hour after notice to remove the same.

15.—All goods, wares, or merchandise conveyed by the Ferry shall be removed from the warehouse used in connection with the Ferry within 48 hours from the time when in the ordinary course of post notification of the arrival of the goods should reach the consignees, and a charge of one penny per day or a part of a day will be made in respect of each article or parcel left in such warehouse after the expiration of the said period of time.

16.—No person shall fasten or moor any vessel, or boat of any description, to any pier, landing stage, stairs, or works of the Corporation, without the leave of the Corporation being first had and obtained, and any person infringing this Bye-law shall, in addition to the penalty above provided, be answerable for all damage which may be done.

The Common Seal of the said Corporation was affixed hereto in pursuance of a resolution of the Council in the presence of

R. GWYNEDDON DAVIES,
MAYOR.

ROBT. O. ROBERTS,
TOWN CLERK.

The Board of Trade hereby consent to and approve the foregoing Bye-laws.

T. W. P. BLOMEFIELD,
Assistant Secretary.

BOARD OF TRADE,
28th September, 1908.

Printed by O. R. Owen, Minerva Printing Works, Turf Square, Carnarvon.

The Carnarvon & Anglesea Ferry Bye-Laws, 1908. [GAS]

PS *Menai*

A new steamer, the *Menai,* built by Greenstreet & Paton, Liverpool for the newly-formed Menai Steam Navigation Company was delivered to Caernarfon in April 1849 where she was enthusiastically welcomed, especially by those who were regular users of the ferry. It was apparent that the new boat had attracted additional patronage since the takings for May, June and July averaged £67-10s-3d when compared to an average sum of £31-10s-1d received per month between June 1848 and the end of April 1849.

Due to a lack of capital and resultant cash flow problems, the company (including the remaining term of the 31-year lease) was sold by public auction in March 1851 to Llewelyn Turner, who was acting on behalf of John Owen of H. Owen & Sons, Market Street, Caernarfon, for £1,075. In 1853, the company bought another steamer the *Prince of Wales*, which assisted in moving ships in and out of Caernarfon harbour in addition to ferrying passengers to Anglesey and operating pleasure trips along the strait.

Although Caernarfon businessmen had succeeded in having the continuing complaints about the ferry service discussed at a public meeting chaired by the mayor in January 1866, the town council still refused to take over responsibility for the service. It maintained this position until 1874 when it eventually decided to buy the ferry rights from the Woods and Forests Department for £458, on condition that Caernarfon businessmen, rather than the ratepayers, raised sufficient monies to cover the costs.

The ferry rights became vested in the Borough Council of Caernarvon on 18 April 1874, subject to the condition of its management by a committee of seven – four members of the Borough Council and three residents from the parishes of Llangeinwen, Llangaffo, Newborough, Llanfairyncwmwd and Llanidan in the county of Anglesey, all of whom were to be appointed from time to time by the Borough Council. The ferry rights extended from Abermenai to a line drawn from Llanidan Church to Llanfairisgaer Church. [Caernarvon Harbour Trust 19/106]. It was leased to George and William Moreton for 21 years from 1 January 1875, at a rate of £325 *per annum*. Included in the lease was the clause that the 'ferry should be worked … by a steam vessel there being also a provision for carrying of animals … but that no animals were to be conveyed on boats containing passengers'. On 1 January1896, the lease was taken up by Captain Owen Lewis for a period of 21 years, at the rate of £30 per annum. From 1874 until 1929, steam ferryboats capable of carrying horses and carts, were being used [GAS XM923/331] and reference was made to 'a substantial new pier on the Anglesey side which will be speedily completed'. [C&DH, 7 August 1875]

Possibly as the result of poor or inadequate maintenance to a vessel, the following report appeared in the *Caernarvon & Denbigh Herald* on 7 April 1877:

> In consequence of an accident to the steamer on Tuesday evening when an iron plate had been blown away and the ferry has since been worked by boats. Good Friday and Easter Monday intervened and many who were anxious to cross here unable to do so while those who went experienced great inconvenience … This hampered the trade in the town as goods intended for Carnarvon were taken to Llangefni and Bangor and people from Newborough and Aberffraw etc went to those places to do their marketing.

Even though improvements had been made to the landing place at Tal-y-Foel, including flooring being made 'to prevent cattle from slipping' and a moveable railing being provided for the sides of Western Pier, complaints continued about the ferry service, the piers, the landing places and the warehouses in Anglesey and Caernarfonshire. [UB BP 7393-4] Captain Lewis was asked to explain why there were so many complaints being made regarding non-delivery of goods by the ferry; a letter from Lake & Company, Caernarfon to the Borough Surveyor, stated that one parcel had been found in the sea and it was suspected that it had been thrown overboard. 'Goods are also refused unless they are trucked by our own men to a portion of the slip which the steamer hands desire'. If attempts were made to load goods on to the ferry by anyone other than the crew, then they were said to have 'threatened to throw both the porter and box overboard if he persisted in putting it aboard'. [GAS XD1-462]

Examples of merchandise being carried by the ferry and the costs were:

22.3.1906 Mr Ethall, Pool Street, Carnarvon 40 sheep, 36 lambs and manservant 4s-5d.
21.3.1906 Robert Pritchard, Penygroes 35 sheep, 4 lambs and 2 men 4s-11d
22.4.1927 Marston Thompson – Hughes, Menai Inn: 1 barrel ale 9d
12.6.1925 Williams, Bodrida – Davies, Blacksmith: 1 trap
11.10.1925 Robert Williams, Ty Main, Newborough – Williams & Owen, Carnarvon: 32 bags oats 12s-3d.
15.10.1925 Roberts, Tyddin, Newborough – Lewis, Chip Shop, Twthill: 10 bags vegetables 2s-6d
20.11.1925 Roberts, Cefn Derwen – Manager, National Provincial Bank Ltd.: 1 bag vegetables 3d
3.12.1925 Roberts, Trefarthin – Electricity Works: 1 battery 3d
16.11.1916 Marston Thompson – Mr Bernard, Menai Hotel – 3 barrels beer 9d
[GAS XD1-478, XD1-481, XD1-482, XD1-483]

The cost for passengers crossing from Tal-y-Foel to Caernarfon subsequent to the takeover by the council was: children 1d, adults 2d, horses 6d, cattle 6d, sheep 1d, pigs 3d. If a four-wheeled carriage and two horses were taken across then the cost was 2s but this was reduced to 1s-6d if only one horse was involved. By comparison, a donkey cart and two donkeys cost 9d. These appeared to be the general charges for all three ferries, but a schedule for 1874 showed that passengers on the Moel-y-Don ferry were only charged 1d for adults and $^1/_2$d for children.

The ferries were well patronised by the people of south Anglesey who were dependent on Caernarfon continuing as their trading town. For those living in the vicinity of Newborough, a trip across to Caernarfon on the ferry entailed a comparatively short walk down to Tal-y-Foel where the ferry affectionately known as '*stemar bach Sîr Fôn*' (the little Anglesey steamer) would be boarded. Amongst those that regularly crossed were youngsters attending school in Caernarfon.

In an attempt to rejuvenate the rapidly declining ferry service, a number of innovations were introduced in the 1930s including 'Frequent trips along the Menai Straits and to Llanddwyn Lighthouse'. Also advertisements appeared in local papers stating 'Caernarvon and Anglesey Ferry – daily service to and from Anglesey by well-equipped motorboats. Parties specially catered for … All particulars from Borough Surveyor, Guild Hall, Caernarvon'.

PS *Mayflower*

Owen Lewis's vessel *Mayflower*, with John Roberts in charge of its daily activities, had, during the two weeks ending 22 December 1894, ferried 1,511 passengers, 801 sacks, 15 carts, 253 boxes, together with cattle, barrels, timber, side of beef, furniture, plough, slate cistern and wheels.

The *Carnarvon & Denbigh Herald* of 7 August 1895 reported on repairs carried out on the Mayflower:

> the ferry has been repaired and a condenser boiler has been added which will render her a very strong and fast going ferry boat. Very shortly arrangements will be completed so that the present inconveniences by crossing in small boats will be remedied and Anglesey and Caernarvonshire brought within fifteen minutes distance. We believe Messrs Morton the lessors intend running the steamer every half hour.

Although the *Mayflower* had been acquired by Caernarfon Corporation, along with the ferry rights, in 1896 [GAS XM923/331, XD1/463] complaints about the ferry service persisted:

> The Anglesey Ferry – For some time past, complaints have been made regarding the unsatisfactory manner in which the above ferry is being worked. The steamer *Mayflower* is now being repaired and the traffic between this town and Anglesey is greatly injured and the comfort of the passengers interfered with. This grievance was a subject of complaint at the last meeting of the town council when it was resolved to convene a committee of the tradesmen of this town together with the Anglesey farmers &c to discuss the matter. The committee met at the Guild Hall on Monday last. Amongst those present were:- Messrs James Rees (chairman), Robert Williams, Brunswick Buildings; Calwaladr Williams, Leeds House; J. Evans, J. O. Griffiths (Ioan Arfon), S. Griffiths, Uxbridge Square; W Williams, Anglesey; H. Williams, cabinet maker; – Hughes, farmer, and others. Complaints as to the unsatisfactory manner with which the ferry is now being worked were made by Messrs R. Williams, Brunswick Buildings; John Abbott, Henry Jones, David Abel and W Williams, butchers all of whom agreed that the present arrangements were detrimental to the trade of Carnarvon. It was also remarked that in consequence of the delay caused by the steamer the farmers on the Anglesey side took their goods to the Llangefni and Bangor markets and that those employed on the ferry were discourteous towards the passengers. As it was explained that the steamer was now being repaired but would be ready by Thursday it was proposed by Mr Evans and seconded by Mr Robert Williams that the meeting be adjourned for some time in order to see how matters would go on.

PS *Arvon*

The 48-ton *Arvon*, powered by a 31hp engine, was built at Rotherglen in Glasgow in 1896 for Captain Owen Lewis, Church Street, Newborough at a cost of £3,300. In a letter to R. L. Jones, the Caernarfon Borough Surveyor, dated 21 November 1895,

PS Arvon *transporting military horses to Anglesey, c.1910. [L. Larsen]*

Passengers disembarking from the PS Arvon *at Caernarfon. Although not a good quality photograph, this picture clearly shows the wide beam of the boat. [FAS]*

Lewis stated 'when I was at Glasgow last week the steamer was far advanced'. Within less than eight years the *Arvon* required 'a new bottom and narrowing of the paddle boxes and wings costing £487'. Her crew in 1913 consisted of E. Griffith (mate), J. Williams (warehouseman), J. Lloyd (AB), Daniel Jones (master) David Davies (engineer) and R. Daniel (toll collector). [GAS XD1-812]

Complaints about the ferry service continued to such an extent that Captain Owen Lewis was summoned to appear before the ferry committee on 16 October 1901 regarding 'irregularities with the ferry service'. He was given a week to consider the matter. When he reappeared before the committee, he offered to sell the PS *Arvon* to the corporation for £3,500. After an independent valuation, he agreed to sell his 'steamer, launch, boats, buoys and all plant connected therewith, together will all its interests in the Tal-y-Foel and Abermenai ferries, for the sum of £3,100'. This was agreed and the deal was completed 15 November 1901. [GAS XD1-811]

In June 1902, the corporation decided to 'Prohibit smoking in the cabin of steamer and in the new waiting room at Tal-y-Foel'. On the assumption that shovelling coal into an engine was no different whether it was on land or at sea, the corporation recommended on 1 January 1904 'that subject to the approval of the Highway Committee, the driver of the steam roller be allowed to go on the *Arvon* whenever convenient and accustom himself to the working of the engine in order that he may be prepared to assist should circumstances require'.

During the 1904 summer season, two-hour pleasure trips on either *Arvon* or *Ynys Môn*, whichever were not engaged in acting as a ferry, were available every Thursday at 3 p.m. at a cost 1s per person; 6 p.m. at 6d each and 8 p.m. at 3d each. Other trips went to Menai Bridge, Bangor or Beaumaris: half-day 1s or £3 for 60 passengers and £5 for 100 passengers (ideal for organised trips). Coal for the vessels was purchased from Point of Ayr colliery in Flintshire for 14s-3d per ton. If both ferries happened to be unserviceable, it was not unknown for the dredger SS *Seiont* to be hired from the

The crew of the PS Arvon, c.*1913. [GAS]*

SL Ynys Môn *ferry at the Victoria Dock, Caernarfon. [GAS]*

Caernarvon Harbour Trust at a cost of £19. There were occasions when, due to the number of animals that needed to be transported, passengers could not be accommodated on the *Arvon*, as was the case on Whit Monday 1903: 'for the conveyance of cattle and heavy traffic only – passengers to be advised'.

As a result of a severe gale on 20 December 1929, when the *Arvon* was crossing to Anglesey, the boat was grounded and the eight passengers on board had to walk ashore as did the crew, Captain Flynn and Henry Williams (engineer) who spent the night in an Anglesey farmhouse. The boat which had been swamped during the night was brought back to Caernarfon by the pilot R. J. Jones on 10 January 1930. During the time when she was being surveyed, the SS *Seiont* was hired for two-and-a-half days. If major repairs were required on the ferries, they would invariably be carried out at the Port Dinorwic dry dock.

SL *Ynys Môn*

The new steam launch *Ynys Môn* was built by H. Pritchard & Rutherford for the corporation in August 1902. During the 1904 summer season the *Arvon* and *Ynys Môn* jointly ran pleasure trips along the Menai Strait every Thursday with other trips to Menai Bridge, Bangor or Beaumaris whenever the demand justified the journey. [GAS XDI812 and *C&DH* 6.9.1902]

PS *Menna*

The *Menna* was built in Queensferry, Flintshire by Abdela & Mitchell Ltd to carry vehicular traffic as well as passengers. Measuring 84ft x 30ft x 5ft 6ins and costing £4,396, she was licensed to carry 216 passengers and a crew of four. The launch date

PS Menna *ferry disembarking passengers at Tal-y-Foel. [AC]*

was planned for the 30 June 1923 but, although the greater part of the machinery had been fitted by then, the boiler was to be 'installed at a later date'.

The actual launch was carried out by the Mayoress of Caernarfon, Mrs A. H. Richards, who was accompanied by her husband, the Mayor. When an application was submitted to the Board of Trade to register the name of *Menai* the council was informed that this was not possible as the name was already registered against another vessel. The alternate name of *Menna* was deemed acceptable. Due to additional costs being incurred

PS Menna *ferry about to cast off from Caernarfon. Note the Morris & Jones warehouse on the right.* [John Lloyd

PS Menna *ferry high and dry on the Aber shore, Caernarfon, awaiting sale, 1920.* [FRO]

PS Menna *ferry after being sold to Pembrokeshire County Council who renamed her* Alumchine. [FRO]

on the vessel it was necessary for the council to borrow an additional £300. It appears that the *Menna* was the last vessel built by Abdela & Mitchell Ltd. [GAS XS3478/365, XD1-760, XM2747 and FRO D/DM/1439]

Having made a profit of £177 in 1925, by the following year this had fallen to £42 and continued to decline. An observation made by the *Caernarvon & Denbigh Herald* in May 1929 stated: 'Cattle and sheep were still carried in abundance' but by the following year the paper's comments had changed: 'The Anglesey Ferry – the traffic continues to dwindle – January tolls £20 as compared to £76 for January 1929 due to the decline in the transporting of livestock (which now goes by road)'. Despite various measures being taken to improve patronage, the number of passengers continued to fall. The *Caernarvon and Denbigh Herald* of May 1929 declared 'Two ferry steamers are now on sale because the motor trade has killed the ferry traffic … The *Menna* – the Caernarvon ferry steamer – is a comparatively new vessel. It cost about £3,000 and the money borrowed has not been paid off.'

Having decided in July 1929 to sell the vessel, the last of the steamers to serve as a ferry in Caernarfon, the *Menna* was put in the hands of boat brokers Thomas McLaren & Co. In the meantime, the local paper described the *Menna* as being high and dry on the Aber shore. She was eventually sold to Pembrokeshire County Council who used her as a ferry (by then renamed as *Alumchine*) between Neyland and Hobbs Point, Pembrokeshire until she was scrapped in 1956.

MV *Sussex Queen*

In 1829, it came to the notice of Caernarvon Borough Council that a boat called the *Sussex Queen* was on sale in Twickenham and, despite the ferry service having made a financial loss, she was purchased for £500. Captain Thomas Flynn and Henry Williams brought her along the canals to Bristol where they were met by Richard J. Jones, the Caernarfon pilot. Under his supervision, the boat was brought by sea safely to Caernarfon.

In August 1929, the local paper announced 'New motor boat in hospital at a time when it was most wanted and causing a loss of earnings'. By November the engine had to be rebored and other repairs, which included restoring the propeller damaged whilst negotiating the canals from Twickenham, were carried out. The eventual cost amounted to about £800. In June 1939, it was decided to replace the engine with a new 36-hp Thorneycroft and, within three months, the vessel was requisitioned by the Ministry of Transport. A couple of months later, the Ministry decided to buy the *Sussex Queen* for £1,200. When she was no longer required for war service, the Ministry offered to sell it back to the council but, since she would require repairs costing £900 before resuming her pre-war duties, the offer was declined.

CARNARVON AND ANGLESEY FERRY.

TIME TABLE.

Month.	GADAEL CAERNARFON. LEAVING CARNARVON.							Mis.	GADAEL SIR FON. LEAVING ANGLESEY.						
	a.m.	a.m.	a.m.	p.m.	p.m.	p.m.	p.m.		a.m.	a.m.	a.m.	p.m.	p.m.	p.m.	p.m.	p.m.
Jan.	7 45	9 15	11 0	1 0	3 0	4 30	...	...	Ion.	8 30	10 0	12 0	2 0	4 0	4 45	...	...
Feb.	7 45	9 15	11 0	1 0	3 0	5 0	...	...	Chwef.	8 30	10 0	12 0	2 0	4 0	5 15	...	...
Mch.	7 45	9 15	11 0	1 0	3 0	5 0	...	...	Maw.	8 30	10 0	12 0	2 0	4 0	5 15	...	...
April	7 45	9 15	11 0	1 0	3 0	5 0	7 0	...	Ebrill	8 30	10 0	12 0	2 0	4 0	6 0	7 15	...
May	7 45	9 15	11 0	1 0	3 0	5 0	7 0	...	Mai.	8 30	10 0	12 0	2 0	4 0	6 0	7 15	...
June	7 45	9 15	11 0	1 0	3 0	5 0	7 15	...	Meh.	8 30	10 0	12 0	2 0	4 0	6 0	8 0	...
July	7 45	9 15	11 0	1 0	3 0	5 0	7 15	...	Gor.	8 30	10 0	12 0	2 0	4 0	6 0	8 0	...
Aug.	7 45	9 15	11 0	1 0	3 0	5 0	7 0	...	Awst	8 30	10 0	12 0	2 0	4 0	6 0	7 15	...
Sept.	7 45	9 15	11 0	1 0	3 0	5 0	...	...	Medi	8 30	10 0	12 0	2 0	4 0	6 0	...	...
Oct.	7 45	9 15	11 0	1 0	3 0	5 0	...	...	Hyd.	8 30	10 0	12 0	2 0	4 0	5 15	...	...
Nov.	7 45	9 15	11 0	1 0	3 0	4 30	...	...	Tach.	8 30	10 0	12 0	2 0	4 0	4 45	...	...
Dec.	7 45	9 15	11 0	1 0	3 0	4 30	...	...	Rhag.	8 30	10 0	12 0	2 0	4 0	4 45	...	...

Carnarvon and Anglesey Ferry Time Table, 1916. [GAS]

ML Ynys Môn. *[GAS]*

ML *Travelia*

Due to the Second World War, the Caernarfon ferry committee had great difficulty in obtaining a replacement ferry boat after the requisition of the *Sussex Queen*. Even attempts to get a local builder to build one failed because of other pressing commitments. Eventually, the motor-launch *Travelia* was purchased from Bangor Council in March 1944 for £92. She was sold in November 1945 for £50, possibly because the number of passengers that she was allowed to carry was limited to twelve. [GAS XD1-809]

ML *Ynys Môn*

It was reported in November 1946 that the *Ynys Môn*, which had the benefit of 'cabin accommodation', was running five days out of six per week since her diesel engine was much cheaper to run when compared to a petrol engine. The now aging *Arvon* took over duties for the sixth day. It also remarked 'the amount of traffic being carried by the boats were [sic] very disappointing and that the Anglesey people were not giving the support anticipated'. A new gear box was fitted to the *Ynys Môn* in June 1953 at a cost of £30 and she was sold the following year to Mr J. Hare of Llanbedrgoch for £65. [GAS XDI 809]

ML *Arfon*

The decision was taken July 1945 to purchase the ferryboat *Rose* for £750 from brokers, Peter Hancock & Sons of Milford Haven. The boat, 33ft long x 10ft beam x 24ins load draft, was carvel-built in 1930 and had a 6-cylinder, 20-hp Morris Commodore engine, capable of producing a speed of 8 knots. She carried a crew of two and was registered to carry thirty-five passengers. On arrival in Caernarfon, she was renamed *Arfon*. Six years later, her engine was replaced and in 1953, the gear box required repairs costing £30. While she was out of service, the *Welsh Girl* was hired to take her place.

In March 1954, the *Caernarvon & Denbigh Herald* published figures showing that

FERRY TOLLS.

The Ministry of Transport having sanctioned the increase of Ferry Tolls, **notice is hereby given** that on and after Friday, August 6th, 1920, the following Tolls will be charged:

	s.	d.	
For each Adult, each way	0	6	
Children, do.	0	3	
Four-wheeled Carriage, 2 Horses	4	0	
Do. 1 Horse	3	0	
Lorry, Loaded (or Empty), 1 Horse, Return Journey	6	0	Same Day.
1 Horse, Single Journey	3	6	
Do. Empty	2	6	
Gig, Car, or Pony Carriage, 1 Horse	2	6	
Donkey Cart with 2 Donkeys	2	0	
Do. Empty, 1 Donkey	1	3	
Horse or Head of Cattle	1	3	
Calf	0	6	
Sheep	0	1	each.
Lambs	0	1	do.
Pigs and Stores	0	8	
Sucking Pigs	0	3	
Grain and Oats, per Sack	0	6	
Do. do. Bag Flour, &c.	0	4	
Mats, Ropes, per Dozen	1	0	
Laths, according to Size	0	6	per Cwt.
Geese	0	1	each.
Cement, per Cwt	0	6	
Porter and Ale, per 54 Gallons	1	0	
Herrings, per Cwt.	0	6	
Sugar, do.	0	6	
Earthenware, do.	0	6	
Wine or Spirits in Bottles, per Dozen	0	6	
Tea per Cwt.	0	6	
Rice, do.	0	6	
Soap, do.	0	6	
Candles, do.	0	6	
Hay or Straw, per Cwt	0	6	
Box, Parcel, &c., according to Size	{ 0	3	
	{ 0	2	
Bale, Large	1	0	
Do. Small	0	6	
Nails, per Cwt.	0	6	
Iron, Slate, Bricks, &c., per Ton	6	0	
Coal and Coke, per Ton	4	0	
Motor Car, Single Journey	5	0	
Motor Cycle and Sidecar	1	6	
Do.	1	0	
Bicycle	0	4	
Hand Cart	0	8	
Wheel-barrow	0	3	
Plough	1	6	
Drill, &c., according to size	{ 2	3	
	{ 1	9	
	{ 1	6	

Dated this 4th day of August, 1920.

Guild Hall,
CARNARVON.

ROBT. O. ROBERTS,
Town Clerk.

Caernarfon–Tal-y-Foel ferry tolls, 1920. [GAS]

ML Arfon *leaving Caernarnfon for Tal-y-Foel, March 1954.* [AC]

the number of passengers being carried by ferry had declined from 41,254 in 1941 to 8,481 by March 1953, resulting in a financial loss which had to be borne by the ratepayers. Initially when the council declared its intention to apply for the discontinuation of the ferry service, Anglesey County Council was very much against it. However, with the realisation that the cost of continuing the ferry service would be prohibitively expensive, they withdrew their opposition. The Caernarvon Corporation Act 1954 having received Royal Assent on 14 June 1954, the following announcement was made:

> Notice – Borough of Caernarvon – Caernarvon Corporation 17 March 1954: That the ferry between Caernarvon and Anglesey will cease to operate on the 30th July 1954. The last service on that day will leave Caernarvon at 5 p.m. and Anglesey at 5.15 p.m. W. P. Davies, Town Clerk, 9 July 1954.

The dubious honour of running the last ferry boat service from Caernarfon to Tal-y-Foel fell to the ML *Arfon* on Friday, 30 July 1954. The boat left at 5.30 p.m. with members of the council aboard. After celebrating the event at the Mermaid Hotel on Anglesey, the boat left at 7 p.m. on its final voyage, thus ending a 700-year service to and from either Abermenai or Tal-y-Foel. The ML *Arfon* was eventually sold for £260 to Captain William Jones of Port Dinorwic. [GAS XDI 809 9c, XM8201/9, XM9739, XC2/6/290, XC2/3/92]

Y Stemar Bach – Y Menai

Mae Stemar Bach Y Menai
Yn lliwio fel y saeth
Yn lle mynd trwy y gwtar
Mae rhedeg ar y Traeth

Mae Dan yn lliwio'n gampus
Ac nid ar Dan maer bai
Fod Stemar Bach Y Menai
Yn Fynych high and dry

Mae popeth yn bur daclus
Ar cwch sydd ar y dec
A'r lifebelts *yn y caban*
Rhag ofn ei mynd yn wrec

Dos arni ddim cwt lliwio
Fel yr Arfon *gynt*
Mae Dan yn gorfod sefyll
Ynghanol glaw a gwynt.

Mae Rolant hefo'r gocos
Ac Ellis merchant fruit
Yn brydlon iawn bob amser
Ymhell cyn canu ffliwt.

Mae Benja ar allt Cerrig Barcud
Ar twrna wrth y tro
A Robaich wedi gwilltio
Yn gweiddi 'Lloyd, let go!'

Gwen Jones

6: The Menai Bridge

AS THE RESULT OF THE ACT OF UNION OF 1800, the celebrated civil engineer John Rennie (1761–1821), who had been responsible for the building of canals, bridges and harbours nationally, was asked by Parliament to report on the best routes and ports for the Irish mail service. The six Irish mail packets operating out of Holyhead at the beginning of the nineteenth century were small vessels of less than 100 tons crewed by around ten men. The time taken by these ships to cross the Irish Sea could be anything between 18 and 40 hours. Rennie's report referred to Holyhead as being:

> … an asylum harbour of the greatest utility' but that the expense 'would forbid at present moment' because 'the greatest inconvenience has arisen to His Majesty's Packets Express Vessels in consequence of the crowded state of the harbour … A Harbour Master should be appointed (11 June 1816) to remedy the inconvenience … he could order smaller classes of vessels into shallow water and so leave room at the entrance for His Majesty's packets and thereby avoid the danger of their running against the rocks at Carreg Modlan. [UB BP345]

Since it was not unusual to have 150 vessels in the harbour at any one time and for 60 or 70 sail to come in or go out on one tide. Rennie proposed extending the pier by 40 feet at a cost of £16,490 and 'building a wet dock to cover 22 acres which would conveniently hold 200 sail of vessels'. The report of the Commander of the Packets Holyhead, stated on 17 July 1815 that they were in agreement with the benefits as stated by Rennie. In an attempt at expediting the work they reported, 'We should observe to your Lordships that the work could not now be discontinued and resumed at a future period without great additional expense as the Diving Bell is on the spot and the railways fixed'.

At the end of the eighteenth and beginning of the nineteenth centuries, a number of schemes had been put forward to try and alleviate the many problems encountered by travellers anxious to cross the Menai Strait in order that they could continue their journey across Anglesey to Holyhead. Amongst the various suggestions was for: 'a timber bridge built on piles, a partial embankment with openings spanned by drawbridges and a stone bridge'. On 1 October 1783, a 'List of Subscribers' was compiled towards defraying the expense of 'an application to the Parliament of England to make an embankment or dam with a lock and drawbridge over and a Cross or Arm of the Sea between the Counties of Anglesey and Carnarvon called the Streights of Menei and a new road thro' certain lands on each side of the said Embankment in order to open a communication with the Great Road leading from England to Ireland etc'. [UB PN 2450] It was even suggested that a petition be submitted to the Irish Parliament for aid to build such an embankment. [UB BP3452B & BP3602]

Such proposals were not without opposition however and the Committee of Navigation of the County of Carnarvon was formed to strengthen the argument against any form of bridging that could present problems to strait shipping. Amongst the objectors to the schemes were Thomas Assheton Smith, Lord Penrhyn and Lord Newborough. Objections were based on the fact that the strait was 'frequented by upwards of Four Thousand Sail of Vessels in the Year, all sea rigged and many of them of very considerable Burthen' whose progress would be impeded by any structure across the strait.

On 9 December 1783, opposition to a possible embankment became organised at a public meeting held in Caernarfon when a committee was formed under the title 'Committee for the Navigation of the Straits of Menai' with Lord Penrhyn, Thomas Assheton Smith and Lord Newborough again the main objectors. It was stated that the underlying objections to change appeared to be the supposition that the Anglesey gentry might gain at the expense of those on the mainland.

Opposition generally continued as was reported on 11 March 1784: 'the Carnarvonshire gentry are determined to oppose any plan to build a bridge at Bangor Ferry' [UB PN 2453] even though a report by two engineers had stated 'that a bridge as is visualised will in no way injure the navigation of the Straits'. [UB PN 2455] Possibly because of his business connection with Parys Mountain, Thomas Williams, MP, of Llanidan, reported to Lord Uxbridge on the 21 March 1786 that 'counsel heard on the Menai Bridge Bill ... The whole House was convinced of the impracticality of the Scheme as well as the dangerous consequences that must result to the navigation of the Straits'. [UB PN 2459] It appears that the lack of progress being made with the Menai Bridge project during 1785–6 was due to the continuing prejudices of the Caernarfonshire gentry who feared that Bangor might benefit at their expense if such a bridge was built.

A report in the *London Chronicle* of 18 March 1786 stated:

> Navigation of the Menai Straits – Engineers and Naval Officers were examined to prove the propriety or impropriety of having a bridge. It was stated that it ought to be rejected by the House as a wild, futile, visionary, utopian scheme.

The Caernarfon Harbour Trust which had been constituted in 1793, decided on 3 March 1802 that it would ask Mr Assheton Smith of Vaynol to present their petition against a bridge. The Trust also decided to seek the support of Lord Boston and the Bishop of Bangor on the assumption that their respective ferries would suffer if a bridge were to be built over the Menai Strait.

Even though seemingly influential individuals continued to object to the proposals, the engineer John Rennie was asked to survey the Menai Strait in 1800 and prepare bridge designs on behalf of the government, a decision greatly influenced by the Act of Union with Ireland which came into effect on 1 January 1800 and the anticipated increase in the traffic between London and Dublin. Rennie submitted two plans. The first was for three cast-iron arches, each with a span of 350 feet and 100 feet above high water. The second was for a single 450-feet arch which was 150 feet high in the centre. Both proposals were to be sited at Ynys Moch. The cost of the former was £290,417 and the latter £31,000 less. However, due to the continuing local opposition and the government being involved in the expensive Napoleonic war, ten years was to elapse before Thomas Telford was asked to submit his design.

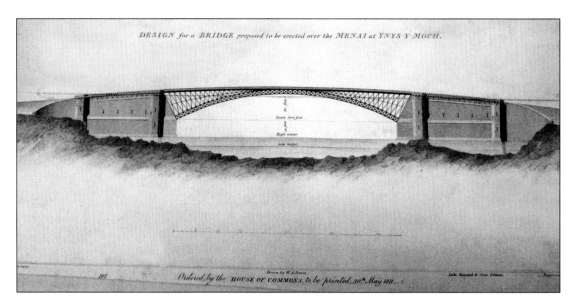

Thomas Telford's design for a single-arch bridge at Ynys-y-Moch, 1811. [UB]

In 1810, Thomas Telford, the renowned Scottish civil engineer was commissioned by the Lords of the Treasury to consider the best method of bridging the Menai Strait. The report submitted by him the following year included two plans: one for a crossing at the Swellies Rock and the other at Ynys Moch. Neither plan was deemed suitable as they did not conform to the Admiralty's directive that any structure had to be one hundred feet above high water overall, so as to allow the many vessels that passed along the strait a clear passage.

As a result of the interest being shown in Telford's proposal for a suspension bridge in Runcorn in 1817, he was instructed to consider a similar design for bridges over the river Conwy and the Menai Strait. The design which he submitted for the Menai crossing was for two main piers, one on the Caernarfon side and the other on Ynys-y-Moch on the Anglesey side, with additional support being provided by three arches on the Caernarfon side and four on the Anglesey side. Two 579-foot-long carriageways, each twelve feet wide, together with a six-feet-wide footpath in between the carriage ways would be supported from sixteen chains and suspender rods. The plans were approved in 1818 and a grant of £123,000 provided by parliament. Ynys-y-Moch had been chosen as it was the narrowest part of the Strait where for centuries drovers had driven cattle to swim across from Anglesey to the mainland.

In the summer of 1818, Thomas Telford and W. A. Provis, the resident engineer, arrived in Bangor and began laying out and building workshops and the construction of quays and piers upon which cranes were to be erected. The influx of workmen, initially 200 men gradually increasing to 400, had a considerable effect on local trade in the village of Porthaethwy. Limestone for the bridge was quarried near Penmon on Anglesey as that rock was considered entirely suitable to withstand erosion from both weather and battering tides. Five vessels, including the *Sally* and the *Swansea* of 60 and 70 tons respectively, transported the stone to the quay near Ynys y Moch. More than 80 men were required to quarry and cut the stone but, despite advertisements placed in national newspapers, difficulties were experienced in recruiting qualified stone masons.

Facing: Thomas Telford's original design for a suspension bridge at Ynys-y-Moch 1817. [UB]

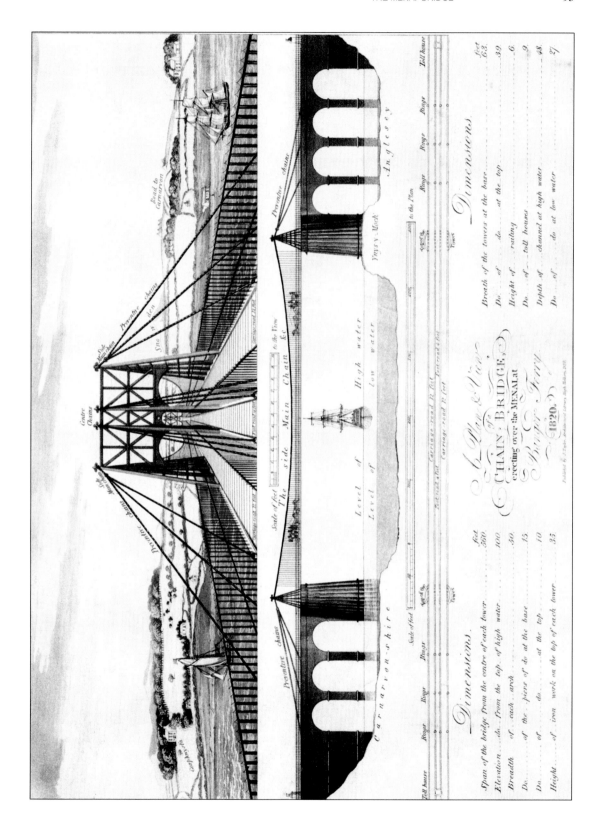

Thomas Telford, FRS, 1757–1834, by S. Lane, In the background of this painting is a depiction of the Pontcysyllte Aqueduct, designated a UNESCO World Heritage site in 2009. [British Museum]

Although Ynys-y-Moch had been levelled for the main Anglesey pillar by the end of August 1818, the first stone, three tons in weight, was not laid until 10 August 1819 due to the shortage of skilled workers. [UB BP3464]

Labourers were paid between 1s-8d and 2s per day, increasing to 4s per day for a foreman. Carpenters and smiths each received a daily wage of 3s-6d. Captains of vessels that transported the dressed stone from Penmon were paid between 2s-6d and 4s-6d per day. Those who had to suffer working in water at the base of the piers were rewarded with ale but, if the weather was particularly bad, were supplied with spirits. In nine days during December 1819, fifty-two gallons of ale were consumed by men working on the masonry.

The Menai Bridge chains were forged by William Hazeldine of Shrewsbury and, to prevent rust, they were dipped in a bath of linseed oil. They were conveyed by barge along the Ellesmere Canal to Chester from where they were brought to Menai Bridge by sea.

With the stonework completed by 1825, the Admiralty authorised that the strait be closed to shipping in anticipation of what was thought to be the most difficult and complicated task of the whole construction, the raising of the chains from a raft 400-feet long and six-feet wide, positioned between the two bridge piers. The first chain was raised from the raft on 26 April 1825 by means of two capstans operated by 150 labourers, and the last was in position by 9 July, with the suspender rods fastened. The wooden carriageways were then installed and the bridge declared completed.

W. A. Provis, his brother John, together with William Hazeldine and others connected with the construction, boarded the Royal Mail coach in Bangor, and at 1.30 a.m. on 30 January 1826, to the cheers of the assembled workmen and the whistling of a gale, crossed the bridge, the reins of the coach having been taken over by Mr Talbot an

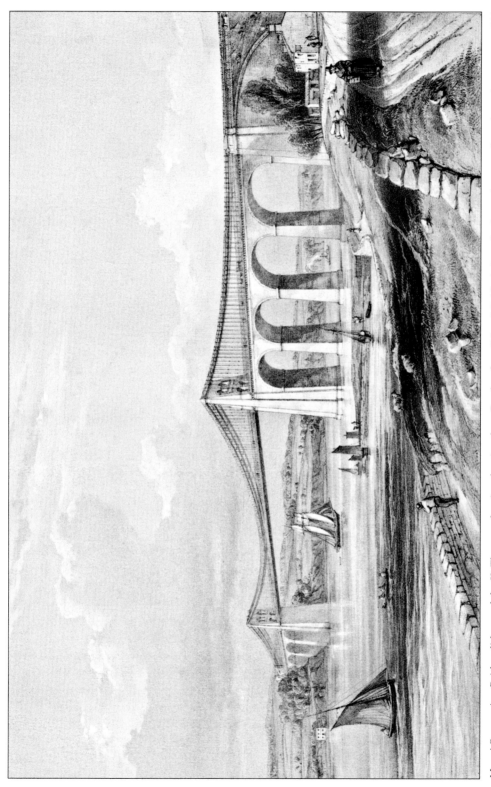

Menai Suspension Bridge, lithograph by K. Thomas, showing the view from Porthaethwy (Menai Bridge). Length of span between the points of suspension, 560 feet, total length 910 feet. Entire length of chain, from the fastening in the rock, 1,710 feet. Total weight of iron, 2,186 tons, 1,280 lbs. Height of roadway above the water, 100 feet. [SM]

Original drawing for the entrance to the Menai Bridge from the Caernarfonshire shore. Note the toll-keeper's box and the tolls displayed under an oil lamp. Even at this early stage provision is clearly being made for high lattice-style railings to prevent pedestrians and horses falling off the bridge.
[SM]

Irish MP. It was stated that 'there was no official opening, but during the day scores of carriages and crowds of pedestrians crossed and recrossed the bridge amidst scenes of great excitement'. As soon as the bridge was opened, the toll collectors took up their positions at the toll booths which would be occupied for 24 hours each day.

The cost of erecting the Menai Bridge was £211,791. One hundred pounds was distributed among the Menai Strait pilots as compensation for loss of earnings during the time when the Strait was closed to navigation (previously approximately 800 vessels of between 16 and 100 tons burden, with occasional larger vessels including 'in one instance a sloop of war', used the Strait annually).

The tolls charged for crossing the Menai Bridge in 1826 were:

Stage and Mail coaches	2s	6d
Post Chaise, Coach. Landau Berlin, Barouche or other carriage with four wheels and four horses	3s	
As above but with four wheels and two horses	2s	
Chaise, Chair, Gig with two wheels		6d
Wagon, Wain or other such carriage with four wheels	1s	
As above but with two wheels		6d
Horse etc not drawing		2d
Foot Passengers		1d
Oxen cows or neat cattle per score	1s	
Hogs, Calves, Sheep, Lambs per score		6d

The number of vehicles and animals that crossed the bridge in the twelve months from 1 May 1844 was:

Coaches with four horses	63	Coaches with 2 horses	1,168
Gigs with four wheels	1,439	Gigs with two wheels	3,607
Carts	8,805	Saddle horses	8,264
Beasts	6,223	Sheep and pigs	10,699

In the following twelve months the figures were:

Coaches with four horses	56	Coaches with 2 horses	1,202
Gigs with four wheels	1.509	Gigs with two wheels	4,022
Carts	9.052	Saddle horses	8,908
Beasts	8.651	Sheep and pigs	14,450
[UB BP6938]			

On 5 July 1825, six months prior to the bridge opening to traffic, an Act of Parliament was passed which ensured that travelling conditions would continue to improve.

Even though the opening of the bridge had facilitated the crossing of the strait and the journey time across Anglesey had been shortened with the opening of a new turnpike road, the number of passengers travelling from Holyhead to Dublin declined in 1826 to 14,413 and by 1831 to 9,020. This was mostly due to the newly founded St George's Steam Packet Company of Liverpool and the City of Dublin Company establishing a new ferry service in Liverpool in 1824 which meant a quicker and cheaper sea crossing to Dublin. The Royal Mail had also transferred its allegiance to the Liverpool crossing, thereby further reducing the numbers of vehicles using the bridge.

For those who made use of the new bridge the question of tolls, and in particular the amount being charged, became a contentious issue even when compared to ferry charges:

Original drawing for the entrance to the Menai Bridge from the Anglesey shore. [SM]

The completed Menai Bridge viewed from the Anglesey shore. The Royal Navy's concern about the passage of tall-masted ships beneath the bridge has clearly been resolved. [BU]

Meeting of the Gentlemen, Clergy and Freeholders of the County of Anglesey 9 June 1823 refers to the tolls to be levied on the Bridge to be erected over the Straits of Menai on the Great Irish Road. That these tolls greatly exceed those on the Ferrymen existing at the same place but which is to be stopped as soon as the Bridge shall be completed. That all the persons passing the Ferry are allowed to re-pass on the same day without additional toll whereas by the same Act they will be liable to pay each time on passing the Bridge which will be a particular hardship on persons living in the adjoining counties. (UWB PN2354)

In an attempt to entice passengers to travel overnight by coach from Holyhead to Shrewsbury, rather than staying in Bangor, an advertisement was placed in the *North Wales Gazette* a few months before the Menai Bridge was opened which stated:

Travelling from Holyhead to London Thomas Spencer, Royal Hotel, Holyhead Respectfully inform the Nobility and Gentry that to avoid the great inconvenience, delay and expense which Passengers by Coach are at present subject to in being detained a night at Bangor on their way to London and the inconvenient hour at which they must again start in the morning (4 o'clock) he has in conjunction with other proprietors established a new Post Coach called The Eclipse which leaves Holyhead every afternoon immediately after the arrival of the Government Steam Packets and arrive at Shrewsbury at six o'clock the next morning in time for the London, Cheltenham, Bath and Bristol Post Coach. Passengers by the conveyance will be out only ONE NIGHT between Dublin and Cheltenham.

A publication issued in 1828 regarding the construction of the bridges over the Menai and Conwy, from the designs by and under the direction of Thomas Telford and

William Alexander Provis, had as its preface the following comment:

> Few works connected with the profession of Civil Engineers have excited so strong
> and general an interest as the Suspension Bridge over the Menai Strait; for though
> the principle of its construction is old as the spider's web, the application on a scale
> of such magnitude, the durability of the materials of which the Bridge is composed,
> and the scientific combination of its various parts, render it one of the highest
> importance for instead of an uncertain Ferry over an often tempestuous Strait at all
> times crossed with trouble and delay and frequently at the risk of life, a commodious
> Roadway has now been established between its shores that can be passed at all times
> with safety and comfort. [GAS XM4373]

The following report on the bridge usage gives an indication of how important it was
especially to agriculture:

> This account does not include any stage coach, every stage coach pays the
> commission to Mr Fisher, there is only one which runs from Holyhead to the Bridge,
> waiting for the packets also one to and from Caernarvon on the like errand. Though
> the list of carriages (with 4 wheels) has been gradually declining, it may be attributed
> to the improvement in the roads generally – the increase on the two wheels (gigs)
> may be said to be in partly the consequence of the Survey of the Railway line through
> the Island – The increase in the number of carts is mostly to be accounted for by the
> dry summer of 1844 and the scarcity of hay and straw in the ensuing winter, this also
> must have had the same effect upon the sale of beasts and sheep, grass and fodder
> being so greatly enhanced in price (in England) as seriously to check the demand for
> cattle at our fairs … the summer of last year being so productive in straw and grass

*The Menai Bridge
viewed from the
Anglesey shore, a view
that was to be
photographed by
countless tourists.
[BU]*

The narrowness of each track on the suspension bridge roadway can be clearly seen in this nineteenth-century photograph. Pedestrians walked on a pathway up the centre of the roadway. [AC]

has increased our traffic over the Bridge last winter which accounts for the great increase on the number of sheep on our last year's list. The number of pigs coming over the Bridge is very small four-fifths of them coming out of Anglesey are shipped off by steamers on the Anglesey side so that the number of sheep of last year's toll may be put at 14,000 an excess of 2,000 on account of the previous dry summer.

The following figures provide an insight into the movement of animals over the Menai Bridge:

	1830	1831	1832	1833
	Pigs – Sheep	Pigs – Sheep	Pigs – Sheep	Pigs – Sheep
Jan	25 – 325	58 – 166	20 – 237	57 – 347
Feb	78 – 349	110 – 430	78 – 523	87 – 291
Mar	180 – 470	107 – 304	83 – 600	127 – 367
April	310 – 276	252 – 312	315 – 411	487 – 879
May	624 – 716	408 – 795	299 – 640	310 – 611
June	199 – 702	2,258 – 510	308 – 904	210 – 672
July	106 – 1,037	88 – 1,327	228 – 1,111	205 – 1,073
Aug	1,233 – 529	1,386 – 762	1,346 – 930	843 – 634
Sept	980 – 740	763 – 1,405	1,040 – 1,007	937 – 912
Oct	2,006 – 1,180	1,533 – 713	1,330 – 1,875	1,618 – 1,270
Nov	572 – 907	427 – 1,236	430 – 276	383 – 591
Dec	99 – 471	220 – 37 60	671 – 73	711

The primary purpose behind the construction of the bridge was to promote and facilitate communication between Great Britain and Ireland. Official documents make no mention of any local requirements or benefits. The paying of a toll to cross the bridge had been raised periodically from the time when it first opened and it was regularly requested that, if the total abolition of the toll was not possible, then a reduction should certainly be considered. Not only would this be of benefit to 'farmers, tradesmen, market gardeners, fishermen and costermongers' who used the bridge on a regular basis to transport goods, but also local people and summer tourists would gain.

Although the railway had reached north Wales by the middle of the nineteenth century, ships, such as the PS *Prince of Wales* continued to carry merchandise from Liverpool to Menai Bridge as the following advertisement which appeared in a local paper indicated:

> … steamer sails from Menai Bridge Mondays, Wednesdays and Fridays at 10 a.m. calling at Bangor, Beaumaris and Llandudno (when weather permits). From Prince's Pier, Liverpool Tuesdays, Thursdays and Saturdays at 11 a.m. The *Prince of Wales* will take cargo on board every Monday at the Clarence Dock.
> City of Dublin Co. Office, Menai Bridge. [*North Wales Chronicle* May 1857]

With the advent of motor vehicles in the early part of the twentieth century, and the increasing weight imposed on the structure, a weighbridge was installed at each end in 1922. Thereafter, passage across the bridge was restricted to vehicles with a maximum weight of $4^1/4$ tons. In addition, vehicles had to keep 50 feet apart whilst crossing the bridge and limit their speed to four miles per hour. These regulations were imposed in an attempt at preventing any undue strain on the fabric of the bridge.

In an attempt to justify the high tolls imposed on vehicles crossing the bridge, it was stated that it was due to the constant need for repairs, servicing and the almost continuous painting of the bridge. During the 1920s and 1930s, the charges of 3s-6d on buses and charabancs and 1s-9d on cars inevitably resulted in fewer vehicles travelling to and from Anglesey. The high tolls also affected the price of goods that were transported across the bridge. Eventually, as the result of vociferous agitation, the toll on cars was reduced to 6d, and buses to 1s-3d per journey in

Photograph of the toll office on the Caernarfonshire side of the Menai Bridge, c.1925. Note the weighbridge set into the roadway in the foreground of the picture. [Alaw Jones]

Workmen painting the Menai Bridge with Dixon's silica-graphite paint, c.1931. [Alaw Jones]

1935. If the weight of a bus, together with that of the passengers being carried, was in excess of the permitted limit, a reduction in the weight was accomplished by requesting a certain number of passengers to alight from the vehicle and walk to the other side of the bridge where the bus would wait for them. Other charges made at this time were Hackney carriages 1s-9d (for each crossing) and invalid chairs for disabled ex-service men 6d.

The case put forward to members of the Chester and North Wales Chambers of Commerce held at Penmaenmawr in 1934 to secure a reduction in the Menai Bridge tolls, was that:

> the excessive toll is iniquitous because it is an additional tax on motorists who already pay heavily for a free and good highway and that it is a stranglehold on the trade of Anglesey and Caernarvon, many industries having been completely wiped out ... the cost of the bridge had been repaid to the Government by special taxes at the time and there was no excuse for charging the public nearly £10,000 a year over and above the cost of maintenance for crossing the bridge ... the meeting agreed to lend support to the demand being made by the Bangor Chamber for a reduction they would help the effort ... The bridge was built in the first instance to develop the good feeling which should exist between Ireland and this country but the need for its use for this purpose had long since ceased and yet the heavy charges for crossing were continued. The Ministry's proposal to provide a new bridge was a good one. The present bridge was not ideal one to meet the kind of traffic that now used it ... the Ministry of Transport had commuted that the length of life of the existing bridge could not exceed six years. The Ministry had contemplated building a new one. Caernarvonshire turned it down because they felt they could not take over the responsibility of maintaining the proposed new bridge without any toll.

During its long years of service, the Menai Bridge has been battered by the prevailing south-westerly gales channelled along the strait. Shortly after it was opened it experienced a strong gale which caused some of the suspender rods to snap. Further

Work gets underway on the rebuilding of the Menai Bridge, 1938. [Bangor Museum]

damage was caused by a bad storm in 1839 when additional support rods were broken and parts of the wooden carriageway were lifted and deposited in the sea. One of the carriageways was soon repaired and back in action, but the other was so extensively damaged that it took months to repair. In 1893, the wooden carriageways were replaced by a steel deck.

As the result of damage caused by a hurricane in January 1936, drastic measures had to be taken as it was believed that the 1826 bridge could no longer cope with either stormy weather or modern traffic. Apart from the carriageway being too light, the chains

The rebuilding of the Menai Bridge, 1938–40. Note the safety fencing along both sides of the suspension chains. [Bangor Museum]

The rebuilding of the Menai Bridge, 1938–40 . Note the precarious workman's cradle device on the left. [Bangor Museum]

The rebuilding of the Menai Bridge, 1938–40 . Business as usual in the toll office at the Caernarfonshire entrance to the bridge. [Bangor Museum]

The rebuilding of the Menai Bridge, 1938–40 . The men working in the restricted space under the main chains are tensioning the upright supports on the safety screens. [Bangor Museum]

The rebuilding of the Menai Bridge, 1938-40 . [Bangor Museum]

The rebuilding of the Menai Bridge, 1938-40 . As well as replacing much of the ironwork, the project also replaced stonework that had been affected by weathering. The new arches seen here are supported by a pier on the right that has not been changed whilst that on the left has been dismantled and rebuilt. [Bangor Museum]

The rebuilding of the Menai Bridge, 1938-40 . Resetting the anchor points of the suspension chains into the rock on the Anglesey side of the bridge. [Bangor Museum]

were too corroded to provide support for the heavy vehicles that made use of the bridge although the maximum weight limit was rigidly enforced.

The consulting engineers, Sir Alexander Gibb & Partners, were commissioned to make a thorough examination of the bridge and duly reported that the only long-term remedy was a complete reconstruction. In 1938, Dorman Long was commissioned to modernise and strengthen the bridge while still preserving the lines and symmetry of Telford's masterpiece. The stonework was still sound and was to be left untouched, apart from a slight widening of the road archway to facilitate the passage of heavy goods traffic. The chains and suspender rods were replaced and a new deck was constructed with footpaths on each side.

This feat of civil engineering, which took place between 1938 and 1940, was on a par with Telford's original construction. Although the latter part of the work was undertaken during the Second World War, with inevitable restrictions, it was accomplished within the estimated time.

With the work completed, the bridge reopened to traffic and pedestrians on 1 January 1941 being free freed from tolls for the first time.

A letter dated 20 October 1939 from the Ministry of Transport illustrates wartime problems that could have arisen when it stated: 'The work of reconstructing the bridge has reached a stage which renders the structure peculiarly susceptible to sabotage'. [GAS XC2-39-24]

If the bridge had been damaged due to enemy action, alternative ways of crossing the strait were described in a memo marked 'secret' that was sent to the two county councils on 30 July 1941: 'Exercise – Anglesey cut off from Caernarvonshire by breakdown of both bridges. Test the arrangements for transporting our troops across the Menai Strait by water in the following five motor vessels:

1. *Sussex Queen* and *Menai* – Caernarvon/Tal-y-Foel ferry service.
2. *Moelydon* – Port Dinorwic to Moel-y-Don ferry service.
3. *Seiont*, Caernarvon Harbour Trust hopper and dredger.
4. *Beta* – Lancashire and Western Fishery Vessel.'

[GAS XC2/6/211]

Thankfully the need to resort to such measures never arose.

Although the reconstruction of the Menai Bridge had improved matters considerably as far as ease of crossing the strait was concerned, the next 30 years took their toll on the structure, due mainly to the increasing number of cars and, in particular,

To reduce the danger of sabotage during reconstruction, Ministry of Transport passes were issued to regular users, such as doctors, to enable them to cross the bridge without hindrance.

The rebuilding of the Menai Bridge was completed on 1 January 1941. Although the project made significant changes to the bridge, aesthetically it appeared unaltered. A careful examination of the outside of the arches on both towers will reveal the construction of a new footpath on the outer side of the roadway which enables wider access for motor vehicles. [Bangor Museum]

The Anglesey side of the Menai Bridge showing the Rock Vaults public house before it was demolished in the mid 1960s to make way for a new traffic roundabout. [Bangor Museum]

the size and weight of heavy-goods vehicles. Evidence of this can be seen where the masonry has been chipped by lorries and buses negotiating the stone arches.

The situation was further exacerbated by the Britannia Bridge fire of 23 May 1970 which caused severe damage to the wrought iron tubes carrying the railway from London to Holyhead across the Menai Strait. Until repairs and alterations to the Britannia Bridge were completed and rail traffic resumed in May 1971, there was an increase in heavy goods vehicles using the Menai Bridge. The addition of a road deck to the railway bridge eventually resulted in a considerable reduction in the volume and weight of traffic using the Menai Bridge.

7: The Britannia Bridge

THE ORIGINAL DESIGN FOR A BREAKWATER AT HOLYHEAD HARBOUR was intended to protect the outer harbour and to enclose 267 acres of water but, because this was considered inadequate by local ship operators, the Admiralty decided to build a breakwater 1.86 miles long which increased the inner harbour area to 667 acres. Between 1846 and 1873, seven million tons of rock were blasted out of Holyhead Mountain and conveyed in tipping wagons hauled by steam-engines to construct the breakwater. The castellated houses still to be seen near the breakwater were built for the engineer James Meadows Rendel who was the engineer-in-charge of the project until his death in 1857 when John Hawkshaw took over.

With the introduction of rail travel in the mid nineteenth century and its rapid extension thereafter, discussions took place regarding the alternative means of transporting the Irish mail which up to that time had relied on road transport. The available choice of a route for a possible rail link between London and Holyhead was limited due to the mountainous terrain of north Wales. The two main, if not the only, routes under consideration were: from London to Shrewsbury and then via Bala to the small port of Porthdinllaen on the Llŷn peninsula, or London to Chester and then along the north Wales coast.

Noted railway civil engineer Irish-born Charles Vignole (later professor of civil engineering at University College, London) was asked to carry out a survey of the two alternatives but, since he considered the north Wales coast route as being totally unsuitable from the outset because of various natural obstacles such as the Afon Conwy, Penmaenbach, Penmaenmawr and, in particular, the Menai Strait, he concentrated his efforts on the route ending at Porthdinllaen. Although such a route was not without its problems, he was totally dedicated in presenting his case in opposition to railway engineer George Stephenson who had been asked to survey the north Wales coast route, initially as far as Llandudno (then known as Ormeshead) with the possibility of developing it as a harbour suitable for the Irish mail boats.

A parliamentary act of 1844 authorised the building of the Chester to Holyhead rail and the development of Holyhead as the port for Dublin. Robert Stephenson, as engineer-in-charge, began a detailed examination of the route, a distance of $84\frac{1}{2}$ miles, on behalf of the Chester & Holyhead Railway Company.

Consideration had to be given to the crossing of the Conwy and, the even more formidable undertaking of crossing the Menai Strait. In the early stages, as an alternative to building a railway bridge across the Menai Strait, some thought had been

Robert Stephenson (1803–59).

Painting by John Lucas (1807–74) of a conference of engineers at the Britannia Bridge, c.1850: Standing L–R: Admiral Moorsom, Latimer Clark, Edwin Clark, Frank Forester, George Bidder, Mr Hemmingway, Captain Claxton, unknown workman, Alexander Ross. Seated L–R: Robert Stephenson, Charles Wild, Joseph Locke and Isambard H Brunel [Courtesy of Institution of Civil Engineers]

given to conveying railway carriages across the Menai Bridge. The idea was soon dismissed when a report stated that 'the passage of connected railway trains would be injurious to the general stability of the bridge'.

Although Stephenson was aware that the Admiralty had rejected Telford's arch design to support a roadway at Menai Bridge, his first design was to support a railway crossing with two arches, each of 450-feet. This was rejected by the Admiralty. The only alternative left to Stephenson that would ensure an overall clearance of 100-feet as required by the Admiralty, was to construct a tubular bridge that would be made out of riveted wrought-iron plates that would be large enough to allow the passage of trains. Such a tube would be supported by three towers, the middle one being built on the Britannia Rock, conveniently sited in the middle of the strait and of the required dimensions for the tower's foundation.

Throughout the period of construction, the Admiralty made it clear that sailing vessels had to be provided with a clear and unhindered passageway. Since Stephenson intended building the four 450-foot tubes as near as possible to the eventual structure, this would obviate the need for scaffolding which could have impeded shipping.

Eighty white-washed houses were built on the Caernarfonshire

Sir William Fairbairn (1789–1874), was employed (along with Eaton Hodgkinson) by Robert Stephenson as a consultant engineer on both the Conwy and Britannia Bridges. He is credited with the concept of using iron tubes to span the gap between the towers.

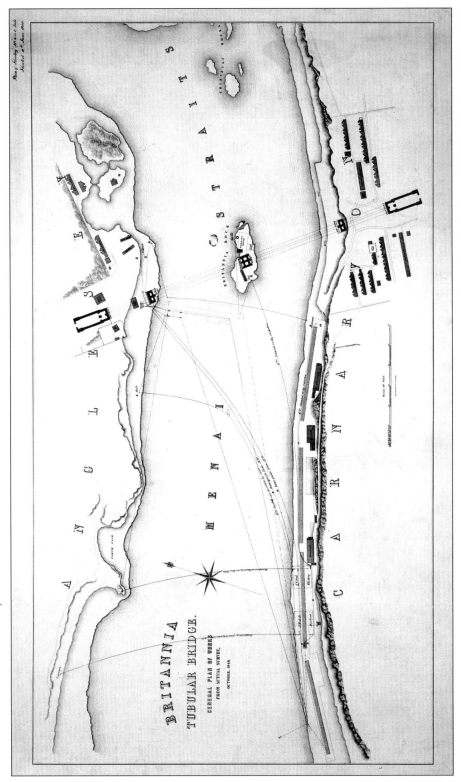

This adaptation of the Britannia Tubular Bridge general plan of works from actual survey, October 1848, shows the plan for floating 'Nᵒ 4' or 'C' tube on 10 June 1850.

side of the strait to provide accommodation for the men and their families. In addition, butcher, grocer and tobacconist shops served their daily needs. A day-school, Sunday-school and meeting house were also provided. The remainder of the recently built village comprised 80 workshops, storehouses and offices.

The first stone of the foundations of the main tower of the bridge was laid by Frank Foster, the resident engineer for the masonry, on 10 April 1846. Work on the main tower foundation, measuring 62 feet x 52 feet 5 inches, which was of stone quarried at Penmon on Anglesey, could only be carried out when tides permitted. The overall height of the tower was 221 feet 3ins and the last stone on top of the Britannia tower was laid 22 June 1849. Work on the other two side-towers, each $177^1\!/_2$ feet high, was also begun at the same time.

Platforms upon which the tubes would be constructed had been built on the mainland shore. Upon these all the building requirements were assembled together with a tramway upon which wagons enabled sheet-iron and other materials to be moved where and when required. The work scene was vividly described in the *Illustrated London News*:

> Steam engines are constantly at work pouring their dense smoke into the air and the clash and din of the huge hammers worked by them, the whirr of the many wheels moved by them and the horrid clang of the hammers of the blacksmiths at the forges with the noise echoing along the tubes caused by the riveters closing the seams of the iron work, produce such an union of discordant noises that to imagine its equal is impossible as far as sound is concerned. Nor is it possible to figure in the mind's eye the multifarious engines of unique design and requirements which occur at almost every step and all perform unexampled operations with the most scrupulous exactitude. Nor are the workmen less striking and peculiar than the engines and implements they guide and weld. Strong and sinewy and thoroughly grimed with smoke and dirt more fitting representatives of Cyclops could not easily be found, and the ease with which the most unwieldy hammers are heaved by them must attest their prodigious strength. The precision displayed by the boys employed in hurling the rivets to the riveters engaged in fastening the seams is truly wonderful. Taking a bolt, red-hot, in a pair of pincers, with a jerk they hurl the bolt to the exact spot where the riveter stands, and whether the latter is on a platform working at the sides of the tube or on the top of it, the bolt falls close to his side with the most unerring precision.

The platforms upon which the tubes were being built had been assembled in such a manner that two flat-bottomed pontoons could be positioned directly beneath them. These pontoons measured 98 feet in length, 25 feet in width and 11 feet in depth and would, when carrying the tubes, draw five feet of water. The two pontoons, which were jointly capable of supporting 400 tons, were fitted with valves to admit water and pumps to discharge it. Each of the four main tubes weighed 1,800 tons and contained 327,000 one-inch rivets. Over two million rivets were required for the entire bridge.

Each of the hawsers that would be used to control and guide the pontoons into position was two miles in length and four inches in diameter and attached to powerful captains 'that were kept afloat by means of water-tight barrels which acted as buoys.

Lithograph by George Hawkins (1819–52) of construction work on the Caernarfonshire shore, May 1849. Note the wooden cabins used as workshops by the construction workers. [SM]

One hawser was attached to either shore, another to each pier and the remainder to the pontoons. Communication between the various participants in the matter of floating the tube was initially effected by the firing of a gun. Each capstan crew of 50 men, having been allocated a letter, A, B, C or D as a means of identification, were given instructions by means of coloured flags of red, blue or white. On 13 June 1849, Edwin Clark, the resident engineer, asked for notice to be given to all vessels of the imminent floating of the first tube. [GAS XD88-4-63]

On the evening of 19 June, with a large crowd of spectators having gathered for the floating of the first tube, the rising tide gradually lifted the pontoons and tube off the shore. However, as it was being hauled, the capstan on the Anglesey shore gave way and the operation was halted, much to the disappointment of the onlookers. Although the capstan was repaired during the night, further attempts the following morning were met with a number of problems causing the operation to be further postponed until the evening. Even then, further difficulties were encountered due to the combined strength of the wind and tide buffeting the pontoons. The tension created on the hawser was such that the

ISOMETRICAL PROJECTION
OF ONE OF THE TUBES
BRITANNIA BRIDGE.

Isometric view of one section of the tube, lithograph drawn by Matthew Forester, 1850. The figures inside the tube give a good indication of the overall size. [SM]

capstan to which it was attached was lifted off its platform. The 472-foot tube was eventually positioned within its prepared recesses, but as soon as the weight was taken off the pontoons, difficulties were experienced in controlling them in the strong current. The accompanying steamer managed to secure one, but the other pontoon, with men still on board, drifted as far as Felinheli, two miles from the bridge, before it was eventually brought under control.

The tube was to be lifted 100-feet to its final position by means of two hydraulic presses, one on each of the towers. As the tube was raised in six-foot stages, prior to permanent brickwork being installed, wood packing was built beneath to prevent any dramatic fall if the presses were to fail. On 17 August, after three successful six-foot lifts, the press on the Anglesey tower suddenly burst and the bottom of the cylinder (weighing $1\frac{1}{2}$ tons) fell on to the tube some 80 feet below causing a deep indentation. Fortunately, due to the precautions taken, the drop suffered by the tube was limited to no more than an inch. The other three tubes were lifted without incident and the

Lithograph by George Hawkins (1819–52) of the tube sections being assembled onto rafts on the Caernarfonshire shore, ready for floating into position below the bridge, September 1848. [SM]

Lithograph by George Hawkins (1819–52) of a tube section being floated into position prior to being lifted between the towers of the bridge. [SM]

Three of the four rather stylised lions being assembled in the large studio of sculptor John Thomas. [BU]

spanning of the strait was completed on 25 July 1850.

Each of the four giant stone lions guarding the portals of the tubes, the work of the English sculptor and architect John Thomas (who had previously worked on Buckingham Palace and the newly-built Houses of Parliament), are 12 feet high, 25ft long and weigh 30 tons. Although no longer as readily visible as they used to be prior to the 1970 fire and subsequent reconstruction, all four are still in their original position. A colossal figure of Britannia was intended for the centre tower of the bridge but cost precluded its construction.

Robert Stephenson, in his book *The Triumph of Science – An Account of the Grand Flotation of one of The Monster Bridge 20 June 1849*, perhaps immodestly described the achievement:

> The Tubular Bridge is pre-eminently a work of our era: it is one of those vast and complicated efforts of skill which no previous period of the world's history could command. No one appears to have dreamed of such a thing before: It is a work which Egypt and the ancients might have been proud of, but could never have executed. The floating operation was the most splendid achievement in our days; and we may justly consider it the triumph of science – the master-piece of human skill and wonder of the nineteenth century.

The first crossing of the Britannia Bridge by train took place on 5 March 1850. In October 1852, Queen Victoria, Prince Albert and the Prince of Wales visited the bridge, leaving the Penrhyn Arms in Bangor at 9.30 a.m. They travelled in coaches over the Menai Bridge to the newly-built railway station at Llanfairpwll where they were met by George Stephenson. Whilst the Queen travelled over the bridge through the tube in the state carriage, drawn by men rather than by an engine, Prince Albert and the Prince of Wales, accompanied by Stephenson, walked on the roof of the tube to the other side.

Not everyone was appreciative of the advances which the advent of rail travel had introduced and as late as 1876, the *North Wales Chronicle* was still deriding the experience:

The royal train prepares to cross the Britannia Bridge in October 1852. Note that the train appears to be on the wrong track. [BU]

Aside from the many benefits which the snorting iron horse has brought in its wake there are certain aspects not welcome to some. The picturesque has been sacrificed to the utilitarian. The old-fashioned mode of travelling by coach and stage had its pleasure and delights as well as its drawbacks and discomforts. The drive along country roads over hill and through dale, the sweep through the village streets with the horn shrilly sounding; the halt at the easy roadside inn seem pleasantly to contrast with the whisking and shaking, occasional lunging into outer darkness and the noise and bustle endured by the railway traveller in those days of grace.
[UB BP3464]

The memorial to the men who died during the construction of the Britannia Bridge. [AC]

A monument was erected at St Mary's churchyard, Llanfairpwll to those who died during the construction of the Britannia Bridge:

> William Blayloc, December 1847
> William Jones, 1848
> Owen Parry, August 1949
> John Thompson, November 1849
> John Williams, November 1849
> William Lewis, March 1850
> David Hughes, October 1850

An early steam train emerges from the Anglesey side of the completed Britannia Bridge. Unattributed engraving from Cyclopaedia of Useful Arts & Manufactures. [SM]

In addition, William Brook, described as the 'Principal Accountant', died of typhus fever, 11 October 1847

Passenger train hauled by Class 5 locomotive 45417, emerging from the east portal. [AC]

Although the tubular form of construction of the Britannia Bridge was considered satisfactory at the time, as late as the 1940s calculations indicated that the structure was still adequate for the loading then being imposed upon the structure. By the 1960s, however, when 102-ton gross laden weight wagons were introduced, the stresses produced, especially when coupled with wind loading, were becoming very close to the limit allowed for wrought iron. Numerous tests were then carried out and it was decided that the wagons mentioned could in fact continue to use the bridge without restriction. Soon after the decision was arrived at, the bridge suffered the disastrous fire.

Maintenance men working inside one of the tubes. [British Rail]

Britannia Bridge Fire

Some time after the completion of the bridge, so as to simplify maintenance of the tubes and to provide protection against the weather, light iron trusses were positioned to support a roof of tarred and felted boards. These covered the full length of both tubes. This was the cause of a fire that occurred on 23 May 1970, severely damaging both tubes of the bridge. The fire is believed to have started amongst the debris of 'old birds' nests' at the Caernarfonshire entrance of the 'Up'

The Britannia Bridge before the disastrous fire, with two of the four lions that adorned it in full view. Although still in situ on the modern bridge, they can no longer been seen by travellers as they are concealed below the road deck. [SM]

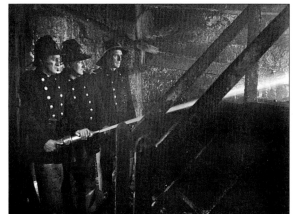

Various views of the serious damage caused to the tubes by the 1970 fire.
[AC]

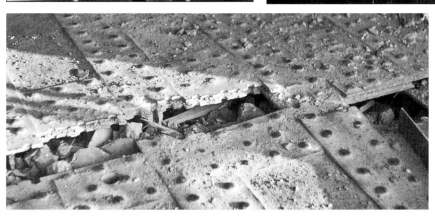

Above: Three local fireman inside one of the tubes using water to cool the hot ironwork.
[E. N. Kneale]

The temporary support put in place under the damaged tubes by men of the Corps of Royal Engineers.
[AC]

tube, between the masonry and the tube itself. The fire then travelled along its full length, and then spread to the second tube until the whole structure was engulfed in flames, no doubt intensified by the multi-layers of tar applied over the years to the hessian covered timber roof. Due to the strong wind that was blowing in the direction of Anglesey, the flames became so fierce that fire fighting was of no avail and the fire had to be allowed to burn itself out and the firemen concentrated on cooling the metal structure to prevent the bridge from collapsing. Although the bridge had been built to allow for expansion and contraction of the tubes in hot weather, the intensity of the fire was such that it soon reduced the tubes to a plastic state, causing both to sag until they were they were in danger of collapsing into the strait. By the time the fire had burnt itself out and the tubes had cooled, the sag was as much as 29 inches in parts and had caused the iron plates to split. Urgent remedial work had to be undertaken before the situation worsened by providing immediate temporary vertical support. This was carried out within days of the fire being extinguished by a team from the Royal Engineers. They filled the slots (which had originally been provided for jacking up the main tubular spans) with eight steel Bailey bridge towers, each of which was capable of supporting a vertical load of approximately 200 tons. By the time these units had been installed in July 1970 the immediate danger of the cracked tubes falling into the strait had been greatly reduced. It was then decided that it would be possible to recover a considerable quantity of rolling stock, which had been marooned on Anglesey as the result of the fire, by means of an endless steel rope system.

A month after the Britannia Bridge fire had occurred, both Anglesey and Caernarfonshire County Councils had expressed their concern as to the effect it would have on the local economy since there was the possibility of the bridge being 'out of action for at least a year'. A memorandum from J. E. Owen-Jones, Clerk to the Caernarvonshire County Council, sent on 14 August 1970 (possibly to the Welsh Office) stated:

> … the need for a second crossing of the straits is certainly warranted on account of the restrictions affecting the Menai Suspension Bridge and the present and anticipated future increased flow of traffic … from a conservation point of view … a second tier on the Britannia Bridge rather than the construction of a third bridge over the straits. From the point of view of congestion in Bangor this project should

A section of one of the steel arches that were built at Port Dinorwic being transferred from the shore onto a barge prior to being towed to the Britannia Bridge. [AC]

The first section of the arch being built in situ. This would bear the weight of the crane that would raise subsequent sections into position. [AC]

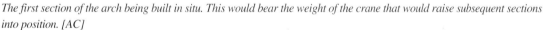

hasten the construction of the Bangor by-pass which would deal with traffic from the A5 and A55.

It soon became obvious that the near destruction of the Britannia Bridge offered an opportunity to provide a second road crossing of the strait.

Since the masonry towers supporting the tubes had not been seriously damaged by the fire, it was decided that they would be retained but that the two tubes between the towers, as well as approach tubes linking the towers to each shore, would be removed entirely. Various methods of achieving this were considered, including the use of a giant floating crane. It was finally decided that two steel arches would be built to support the two main tubes prior to their removal. The steel sections that formed part of these arches were prefabricated alongside the old tidal harbour at felonies. Once completed, the sections were transferred to pontoons (measuring 80 feet x 60 feet) which were towed to the bridge and positioned where they could be raised by crane into the next allocated position. This procedure was repeated until the two arches were complete.

Each tube was then removed in 15-feet sections (each weighing 30 tons). A trestle tower on a bogie carriage was positioned inside the tube by means of a diesel locomotive and then jacked into place against the top of the tube. Once the weight of the section had been taken by the carriage, the tube sides were then cut free from the base using oxyacetylene cutters. This allowed the whole section to be moved along the railway to a point where it could be lifted by crane and placed on the ground where it was later cut into smaller pieces. A new rail deck was then placed directly onto the new arches. Once this was in place, the second tube was removed utilising the same method but this former trackway was then used as a route giving access to the whole length of the bridge to various services. Once this was completed, a new road deck, the full width

The second section of the steel arch being raised into position. [AC]

An arch section is positioned below the Britannia Bridge ready for lifting into position. [AC]

Sections in place on both sides of one of the supporting towers. [AC]

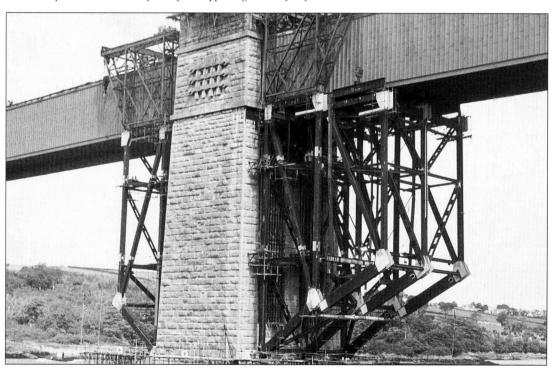

of the bridge, was built directly above the railway and the access route which would eventually form part of the A55 road between Chester and Holyhead.

The reconstruction of the Britannia Bridge and connecting roads took ten years and cost £5.5 million. Two construction workers lost their lives and their names were added to the memorial in St Mary's churchyard, Llanfairpwll: Graham Parry, aged 24, of Trefollwyd Goed, Rhosmeirch, February 1972, and William Owen, aged 47, of 22 Bryntirion, Penisarwaen, February 1973.

The Britannia Bridge was opened to road traffic in May 1980.

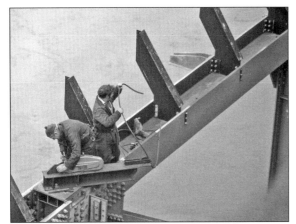

Above left: Preparing the protective side screen. [AC]   *Above right: Crane maintenance high above the Strait. [AC]*

Below: The main arch bearing. Each stainless-steel pin carries a load of approximately 2,500 tons. [AC]

The last section of the arch is raised into position. Once this was done, work began on dismantling the two tubes. [AC]

Above (left): Removal of the tube base. [AC] Above (right): The railway deck nearly ready for the laying of the track. [AC]
Below: The railway service between the mainland and Anglesey was resumed on 30 January 1972. [AC]

The completed arch, supporting pylons. The top deck, which would carry road vehicles, is nearing completion. [AC]

8: Pleasure Steamers

BY THE EARLY PART OF THE NINETEENTH CENTURY pleasure steamers were providing passengers the opportunity to enjoy a scenic sea passage from Liverpool along the north Wales coast as far as Caernarfon. In addition, according to company advertisements, the early vessels carried goods, horses and carriages, no doubt a pleasant alternative to the tedious and uncomfortable journey by road along the coast.

A newspaper report referring to the pioneer voyage of the packet *Albion* on 13 June 1822 stated: 'sailed from Liverpool and arrived opposite Bangor ferry where she remained for two hours so that the party on board might inspect the stupendous work now in progress for the new chain bridge [Menai Bridge]'. Thereafter the *Albion* continued visiting on a regular basis every Tuesday, Thursday and Saturday. The ship was later joined by the *Cambrian* and the *Druid* steam packets and by July 1831, the *Eclipse* (master James Galt) sailing from Liverpool to Caernarfon, calling at Conwy, Beaumaris and Menai Bridge, at a cost to passengers of 1s-6d for a cabin and 1s on deck.

The St George Steam Packet Company, established in Liverpool in 1821, was the first of the notable companies to operate steamers along the north Wales coast. Commencing in 1836, the company's 75hp *Prince Llewelyn*, sailed at 9 a.m. from Liverpool Pier Head on Mondays, Wednesdays and Fridays, calling at Beaumaris, Bangor and Menai Bridge. The voyage took an average of six hours at a cost to passengers of 10s-6d for a cabin or 5s on deck. The return journey could be made on the *Vale of Clwyd* (under the command of Captain Poole) which departed from Menai Bridge on Tuesdays, Thursdays and Saturdays at 9 a.m. The overnight stay provided passengers with the opportunity of local sightseeing or, no doubt for some, a chance to recover from the voyage when adverse weather prevailed.

It appears that some passengers were disillusioned with the conditions aboard the *Prince Llewelyn* and the *Vale of Clwyd* which were described as 'shameful hulks devoid of shelter or accommodation other than a small cavern aft and what screen there might have been on the lee side of a singularly tall funnel'. As a result of this, a new company was formed on 30 June 1830, called the Isle of Man Steam Packet Company Ltd which took over the vessels. By April 1843, both the *Prince Llewelyn* and the *Vale of Clwyd* had been transferred again, this time to the City of Dublin Steam Packet Company, when that firm took over the Welsh service.

The iron *Prince of Wales* was built for the City of Dublin Steam Packet Company by Tod & McGregor in 1849. She measured: length 176.3ft, beam 25.3ft and depth 12.4ft. Her gross tonnage was 328 and she was powered by 200 h.p. engines. Originally fitted with three masts, the mizzen was removed in 1851. After 37 years service, she was sold for breaking up in July 1883.

To ease the berthing of pleasure steamers that had become a regular feature along the north Wales coast and to facilitate the transfer of passengers between ship and shore, piers were built at Llandudno, Beaumaris and Menai Bridge. Passengers wishing to visit Bangor could only do so, depending on the weather, by being transferred to and from shore in smaller vessels in what could only be described as a hazardous and time-consuming operation. Figures published in 1892 showed that 70,000 passengers had disembarked at Menai Bridge but only 10,000 at Bangor due to inadequate facilities.

The pier that was eventually built in Bangor in 1896 enabled the Liverpool & North Wales Steamship Company vessels *St Elvies* and the *Snowdon* (built by Laird Bros for the Snowdon Passenger Steamship Company in 1892) to call at Bangor twice a week. The *Snowdon* was replaced by the *St Tudno* in 1904. Due to the increasing popularity of the voyage from Liverpool to the Menai Strait, the company decided in the same year to increase its fleet by commissioning the *La Marguerite*. This vessel, which was capable of carrying over 2,000 passengers, was scheduled to sail daily as far as Menai Bridge. With the benefit of a pier, Bangor was now able to compete on an equal basis with other coastal towns and, between 1897 and 1914, an average of 34,000 passengers used the city's facility annually.

The variety of services that had become popular by the twentieth century included combining a sea voyage with the return journey by rail:

> Easter Good Friday to Monday April 10th to 13th and Daily from May 23rd to September 21 1936. Steamer *St Tudno* or *St Seiriol* leaves Liverpool 10.45 a.m. due Llandudno 1.05 p.m. and Menai Bridge 2.30 p.m. – Combined rail and sea excursion bookings, also occasional day trips to Caernarvon from Llandudno by new motor vessel *St Silio*.

PS *St Trillo*

Built in 1876 by Barclay, Curle & Company for the Southampton, Isle of Wight and South of England Royal Mail Steam Packet Company, the *St Trillo I* was capable of attaining a speed of 12 knots. Her dimensions were 165.7 feet in length, 20.1 feet beam, 8 feet in depth and 164 tonnage. Pleasure steamers that made use of local piers had the choice of paying the appropriate local authority dues based on the number of passengers being landed and embarking or a flat rate of £20 for the season as was the case with

PS Rhos Trevor, *renamed the* St Trillo *in 1908.*
[James Roberts]

PS Rhos Colwyn.
[James Roberts]

Carisbrooke making use of the Caernarfon pier in 1906 (photo shows PS *Carisbrooke* off the Isle of Wight).

The *Carisbrooke* was acquired by the Colwyn Bay & Liverpool Steam Ship Company at the end of the 1906 season before being sold the following year to the Mersey Trading Company which operated the vessel along the north Wales coast under her new name of *Rhos Trevor*. As a result of the company ceasing to trade, she and another ship, the *Rhos Colwyn,* were sold in November 1908 to W. Hawthorn who, in turn, sold the *Rhos Trevor* the following May to the Liverpool & North Wales Steamship Company who renamed her the *St Trillo*. After a period as a mine-sweeper during the First World War, she returned to the Welsh coast in 1919. In July 1921, whilst returning from a visit to Caernarfon, she struck a rock in the Swellies and remained fast. Some of the 200 passengers on board were transferred to the PS *Snowdon* and PS *Greyhound*. She slipped off the rock with the rising tide and put into Port Dinorwic harbour with some passengers still on board. She was sold by the company at the end of the season.

PS *La Marguerite*

Built by the Fairfield Shipbuilding and Engineering Company in 1893 for Palace Steamers, *La Marguerite* carried passengers between London (Tilbury Pier) and Boulogne, calling at Margate on route. However, her speed and size proved to be contrary to Thames Conservancy regulations and, although popular with passengers, she was not profitable. Her dimensions were length 330 feet, breadth overall 73 feet and depth 21.6 feet with gross tonnage at 1,554. Her compound diagonal-type engines driving the paddles produced a speed of 21 knots. In 1904 she was sold to the Liverpool and North Wales Steamship Company which ran her on the Liverpool–Menai Bridge service. Being the largest of the company's fleet, she was licensed to carry 2,077 passengers. In March 1915 she was requisitioned by the Admiralty for transport duties. During her war service, whilst under the command of Captain John Young, she voyaged over 52,000 miles (mostly at night and without the benefit of lights) carrying over

PS La Marguerite *leaving Menai Bridge.* *[Keith Morris]*

PS La Marguerite *at the Menai Bridge regatta.* *[John Hughes]*

PS La Marguerite disembarking passengers at Beaumaris. *[Nanno Hughes]*

Beaumaris Pier. Note the handcarts used to transport luggage. [Rachael Williams]

360,000 troops between Southampton and various French ports. After being derequisitioned in April 1919, she was initially chartered by the Isle of Man Steam Packet Company before resuming her peacetime role on the Liverpool to north Wales run on 22 May 1920. She made her last trip 28 September 1925 before being broken up.

PS *St Elvies*

Paddle steamer *St Elvies*, built in 1896, was capable of carrying 991 passengers. She undertook excursions from Liverpool to Menai Bridge and around Anglesey, as well as between Llandudno and the Isle of Man. She was requisitioned by the Admiralty in March 1915 for minesweeping duties in the North Sea. She resumed her peace-time role on the Welsh coast in March 1919 where she remained until September 1930 when she was sold to R. Smith & Sons of Liverpool for breaking up.

PS St Elvies *leaving Liverpool for north Wales. Note the unusual cowlings on what were her third set of funnels. [GAS]*

PS St Elvies *leaving Bangor pier en route to Menai Bridge. [ARO]*

PS *Snowdon III*

Described as a 'smart-looking steamer' the *Snowdon* was built in 1892 by Laird Brothers of Birkenhead for the Snowdon Passenger Steamship Company. She operated short runs on Sundays, but went as far as Caernarfon and around Anglesey or north to Blackpool or Douglas on weekdays. Her dimensions were: length 167.9 feet, beam 24.6 feet and depth 10.7 feet and gross tonnage 338. Her two-cylinder compound diagonal engines gave her a speed of 14 knots. When she was acquired by the Liverpool & North Wales Steamship Company in 1899, the decision was taken to operate along the north Wales coast in conjunction with the company's two other paddle steamers, the *St Tudno* and the *St Elvies*. After being requisitioned by the Admiralty to act as a minesweeper in the English Channel during the First World War, she returned to continue with her peace time duties in north Wales where she remained until her days were ended in 1931 when she was sold for breaking up at Port Glasgow.

PS Snowdon III *on the Menai Strait. [Jim Roberts]*

PS Snowdon III
*disembarking
passengers at
Caernarfon. Note the
angle of the ship,
caused by the
passengers gathering
togeher on the port side.*
[AC]

*The officers of the PS
Snowdon III.*
[K. Limerick Jones]

PS *Bonnie Princess*

Measuring 240 feet in length, 26.2 feet beam and depth 9.3 feet, the PS *Bonnie Princess* was built in 1882 for the Liverpool, Llandudno & Welsh Coast Steamboat Company by T. B. Smith & Company of Rutherglen, Scotland. With a gross tonnage of 434, she was powered with diagonal oscillating two-cylinder engines built by A. Campbell & Son of Glasgow. The *Bonnie Princess,* was sold to the Hastings St Leonards & Eastbourne Steamship Company for service along the south coast which continued until 1899 when she was sold to Dutch ship breakers.

PS *St Tudno*

The paddle steamer *Cobra*, built by Fairfield Shipbuilding & Engineering Company in 1889 for the Burns Line, was acquired by a Mr R. Barnwell, who was connected with Fairfield, the following year. Her steel hull measured 264.8 feet in length, 33.1 feet beam, depth to main deck of 14.7 feet and a net tonnage of 412. He renamed her the *St Tudno* prior to operating her along the north Wales coast. The steamer sailed from

PS Bonnie Princess
near Beaumaris,
c.*1920.*
[Rachael Williams]

Liverpool daily except Sundays at 10.30 a.m., arriving at Llandudno two hours later, followed by Beaumaris at 1.40 p.m. and Garth Ferry (as it was described prior to Bangor pier being built in 1896) at 1.45 p.m. before returning to Liverpool by 6.30 p.m. Passenger fares were 6s first class return, and 4s second class return. As the result of the newly-formed North Wales Steamship Company selling the *St Tudno* to Hamburg-Amerika Line in 1891, her name reverted to *Cobra*. She was sold to German ship breakers in 1922.

PS St Tudno (*formerly the PS* Cobra) *went into service in 1890.*
[Jonathon Evans]

Officers and crew of the
PS St Tudno *1896.*
[Jonathon Evans]

PS *St Tudno II*

Subsequent to the *St Tudno I* being sold, the North Wales Steamship Company placed an order with the Fairfield Shipbuilding & Engineering Company for a vessel that would have the benefit of greater passenger facilities and a faster speed. With a length of 264 feet, beam of 32.6 feet and depth of 11.4 feet, she was named *St Tudno II* and launched 9 April 1891. With a gross tonnage of 794, she was certified to carry 1,061 passengers. Her compound direct-acting engines drove the two paddle wheels to produce an average speed of 19 knots and the bow rudder improved her handling capability especially when berthing. She was also sold to the Hamburg-Amerika Line in 1912 for use as a tender at Southampton until requisitioned in 1914 at the outbreak of the First World War for a similar purpose. After resuming her peacetime role for a short while she was broken up in 1922.

PS St Tudno II,
Launched 1891. She
carried 1,086
passengers.
[AC]

MV *St Tudno III*

Built by Fairfield Shipbuilding & Engineering Company, the *St Tudno III* was launched in February 1926 and was certified to carry 2,493 passengers. 329 feet in length, 44.1 feet breadth and 13.6 feet in depth to the main deck, her twin turbine engines produced 4,100 b.h.p. giving her a speed of 19 knots. With Captain W. Highton, DSC, in command, she sailed on her maiden voyage from Liverpool to Llandudno on 22 May. Although paddle steamers had been able to negotiate berths at Beaumaris and Bangor in the past, getting a screw vessel such as the *St Tudno* alongside the respective piers presented difficulties. When passengers wished to disembark at Beaumaris or Bangor, they were transferred to the Bangor Corporation ferry *Cynfal* while the ship was in motion and embarked by the same method. This method of transferring passengers was only carried out for a short period of time due to the inherent dangers. The pier at Menai Bridge however presented no problems for either ship or passengers.

MV St Tudno III,
*leaving Liverpool on
her maiden voyage to
north Wales, 1926.
[Emyr Wyn Roberts]*

Like many other ships, the *St Tudno III* was requisitioned in 1939 by the Admiralty to carry out duties as a depot ship for mine-sweeping operations until March 1946 when she was refitted by her builders in time for the summer season. When she sailed from Liverpool to Menai Bridge on 8 June 1946, under the command of Captain J. Cullen, it was as a one-class boat rather than having passengers segregated into first and second class as had been the case in the past.

At the end of the 1960 sailing season which had been marred by bad weather and industrial disputes, a newspaper reported:

> Dunkirk skipper makes his last trip – The *St Tudno* of the Liverpool and North Wales Steamship Co. left on her last trip of the summer to Llandudno and Menai Bridge after a season marred by bad weather and labour troubles. The ship had been affected by the two unofficial seamen's strikes, the first of which held it up for a fortnight. During the present strike the *St Tudno* has managed to keep doing, although the sailings of her sister ship, the *St Seiriol* have been seriously

MV St Tudno III, *at Menai Bridge.*
[Jim Roberts]

interrupted. Apart from being a sad occasion as the last voyage of the summer, Sunday's trip was also a sad one for the master of the *St Tudno*, sixty-four year-old Captain Robert Dop. After a lifetime spent sailing the North Wales coast, he is retiring. Captain Dop has served the company for 40 years and has been master of the *St Tudno* since 1949. He was born at Port Dinorwic, North Wales, and became master of the *St Seiriol* in 1933.

MV *St Tudno III* continued sailing along the north Wales coast until 16 September 1962 when the service was withdrawn.

MV *St Seiriol II*

The *St Seiriol II* was built in 1931 and was 269.7 feet in length, had a breadth of 37.1 feet and a depth 19.4 feet; she sailed on her maiden voyage from Liverpool to north Wales on 23 May of that year. Capable of carrying 1,586 passengers, due to her stability at sea, the ship was especially popular on the Isle of Man run and for the short cruises that she made from Llandudno. Her geared Parsons Type turbine engines, driving twin screws, produced 3,300 b.h.p. which gave her a speed of $18^1/2$ knots.

The *St Seiriol II* was requisitioned by the Admiralty at the beginning of the Second World War and repainted in war-time grey. As the result of the German army over-running the greater part of Europe, the remnants of the British and Allied forces were confined to a small area around the port of Dunkirk. The *St Seiriol*, together with a variety of other vessels, both large and small, was ordered to evacuate personnel from the port and nearby beaches. Under the command of Captain Robert Dop, the *St Seiriol II* was the first ship to arrive. Although the ship was attacked on a number of occasions and suffered damage and casualties, Captain Dop managed to bring the ship back on two occasions. In recognition of the bravery displayed by the captain and his crew, a plaque, presented by Ronal Gross, Minister of Shipping, was placed near the entrance of the *St Seiriol II's* saloon.

MV St Seiriol II.
[AC]

Captain R. Dobb [sic], Master of the *St Seiriol* 17 June 1940
I write on behalf of the Government to convey to you and to members of your ship's company the gratitude and admiration felt for the help freely given and the courage and endurance displayed by you all in the evacuation from Dunkirk. This operation, in which the Merchant Navy joined as partner of the fighting services, was carried to a successful conclusion in the face of difficulties never before experienced in war. I am proud to pay tribute to your share and that of your ship's company in a great and humane adventure destined to occupy a place of honour in the pages of history

After derequisitioning, the *St Seiriol II* was converted to a one-class ship before resuming her peacetime role 19 April 1946 with Captain Dop remaining in command.

MV *St Trillo II*
Originally named *St Silio* and capable of carrying 568 passengers, the *St Trillo II* was built by Fairfield Shipbuilding & Engineering Company and made her first voyage to

Captain Robert Dop.
[AC]

MV St Trillo II passing the former George Hotel.
[Katie Lench]

north Wales on 27 May 1936. Measuring 149.2 feet in length, with a breadth of 27.1 feet, a depth of 10 feet and a gross tonnage 314, she was powered by twin diesel engines manufactured by Crossley Brothers of Manchester that produced 300 b.h.p. and a speed of 12 knots. Although possessing two funnels, her forward stack was in fact a dummy. She was the first diesel passenger ship to sail along the Welsh coast. After a period of war service for the Admiralty, she was released in 1945 when her name was changed from *St Silio* to *St Trillo II* and the opportunity taken for passenger facilities to be modernised in time for her first post-war trip on 19 May 1946. The ship continued operating along the north Wales coast until Liverpool & North Wales Steam Ship Company ceased trading in 1963 and she was sold to P. & A. Campbell who operated her until 1969.

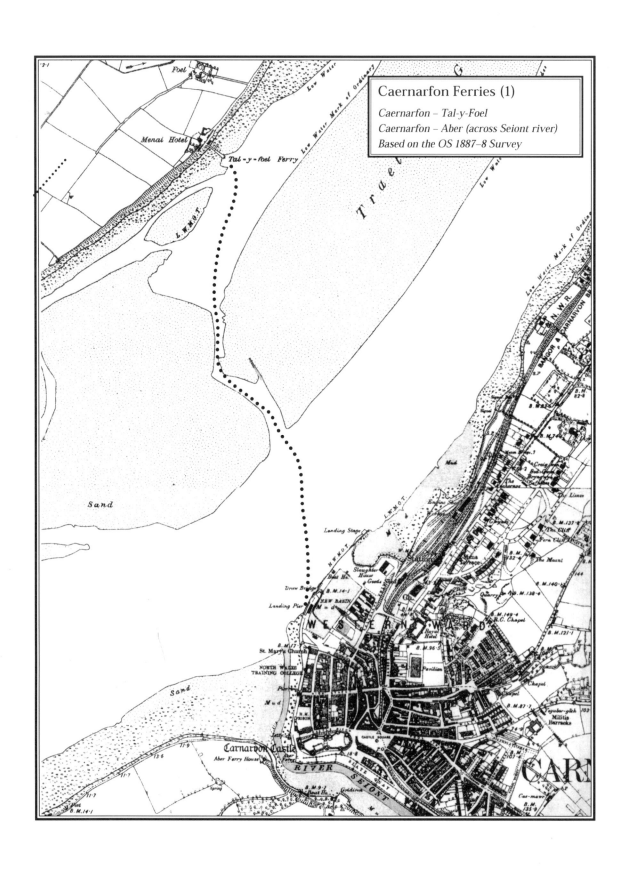

Caernarfon Ferries (1)

Caernarfon – Tal-y-Foel
Caernarfon – Aber (across Seiont river)
Based on the OS 1887–8 Survey